NUCLEAR WAR **THE FACTS** ON OUR SURVIVAL

NUCLEAR WAR THE FACTS ON OUR SURVIVAL

Peter Goodwin

The Rutledge Press
New York, New York

Published in the United States of America, 1981 by
The Rutledge Press, A Division of W. H. Smith
Publishers Inc., 112 Madison Avenue, New York,
New York 10016

First Printing 1981
Phototypeset by Tradespools Limited, Frome,
Somerset, England
First published in the United Kingdom by Ash &
Grant

Library of Congress Cataloging in Publication Data

Goodwin, Peter.
   Nuclear war, the facts on our survival.

   1. Atomic warfare.   2. Survival skills.   I. Title.
UF767.G624   355'.0217   81-8620
ISBN 0-8317-6457-0   AACR2
ISBN 0-8317-6458-9 (Pbk.)

Contents

Introduction

For most of us, nuclear war is unthinkable in the most literal sense — something beyond thought. In this fourth decade of the nuclear age, it is tempting to assume that a nuclear exchange won't take place and that, in any event, there is nothing the average human being can do about it. But the fact is that a nuclear war could happen and very well may happen unless we, as citizens of a threatened world, decide that we will do something.

For this reason, Peter Goodwin's book deserves a thoughtful reading. It is difficult for me to believe that any rational individual who gives it that reading could thereafter accept bland pronouncements that nuclear weapons can serve to advance U.S. foreign policy objectives, that nuclear war can be waged rationally, and that there can be a victor. His analysis of the heat, blast, and radiation effects of nuclear weapons is grim proof of the validity of his basic thesis: "Nuclear war *must* be prevented."

The fact that a nuclear war between the United States and the Soviet Union is not a war either can fight, survive, and win is, I am convinced, not a matter about which reasonable minds can differ. There may, of course, be nuances of difference as to how nuclear hostilities can best be prevented. I, for example, share Mr. Goodwin's concern about the stability and viability of deterrence. I would, however, question his assertion that "deterrence cannot work if everybody agrees that the weapons are too dangerous to use."

As I see it, the weapons are too dangerous to use only because the certainty of retaliatory devastation currently serves as an effective deterrent. And until a better alternative can be found, we must concentrate on making deterrence work.

The problem, of course, is that quantitative additions and qualitative "improvements" steadily make the nuclear arsenal of both sides more deadly and, at the same time and indeed as a consequence, more vulnerable to the other side's first strike. What makes the danger even more acute is that, while some of us put the subject out of our minds, there are others who give increasing currency to the idea that a nuclear war can be won and that our country should prepare itself to do just that. What adds a further dimension to the danger is that some of these people, whom I would describe as pseudo-realists, either occupy or advise people in high positions, both here and elsewhere in the world.

I accept a simple, central thesis — that nuclear weapons can serve only one purpose, and that is to prevent any other country from using theirs against us or our friends. Accordingly, their utility for wider purposes of American foreign policy is nonexistent.

This thesis is, regrettably, not universally accepted. Ever since the first primitive atomic bomb was invented, efforts have been made to find a way in which this vast new power could be usefully exploited by those who possess it. Initially, in the years when we had a nuclear monopoly, we were able to talk confidently about "massive retaliation." Other nations would have to be careful about challenging our interests because of our proclaimed willingness to blow them up if they ventured to do so. In those halcyon days, there were discussions of preemptive nuclear strikes — first against Russia and then against China. And even after the Soviet Union developed its own nuclear weapons, there remained a residual affection for the idea that our threat to use our nuclear weapons could be employed rationally and successfully in the defense of our security.

The growing realization that resorting to our strategic nuclear weapons against targets in the Soviet Union would only mean our own destruction from a Soviet retaliatory strike has dominated our strategic thinking since the 1960s. But there have always been some American theorists who have struggled to escape this straitjacket on our ability to exploit a nuclear military potential. And during the past couple of years there has been a strong upsurge in the view that a nuclear war may well have to be fought and that we should develop and optimize our nuclear weapons and our strategic doctrine so that we can fight, survive, and win such a war.

In his recent book, "The Present Danger," Norman Podhoretz, Editor of *Commentary,* urges that we Americans get over our "inordinate fear" of nuclear war. Former Secretary of State Henry Kissinger, in a blurb for Mr. Podhoretz's book, calls his arguments "unanswerable." I'd put it differently. To me, the argument that we should accept the notion of nuclear war is not unanswerable, it's unspeakable folly.

There are other examples of a growing complacency about nuclear war. Herman Kahn, Director of the Hudson Institute, is quoted as saying that those who view nuclear war as inherently suicidal are, in his term, "crazy." According to Dr. Kahn, "if twenty million Americans were killed there would be two-hundred million survivors." Secretary of State Alexander Haig, in his confirmation hearing, spoke of the "backdrop" of our nuclear strength and said that: "[T]his backdrop serves to strengthen American diplomacy, to enable the American President to speak authoritatively," even at lower levels of tension. And Secretary of Defense Caspar Weinberger, during his confirmation hearings, was asked whether he might have recommended the use of nuclear weapons in Vietnam. He replied: "Any time you get into a war the possibility that you will use every weapon available has to be left open." If we commit U.S. forces, he continued, "we owe it to them . . . to be ready to utilize the strength that we have."

This misguided enthusiasm for nuclear arms is, I should note, bipartisan in origin. Presidential Directive 59 was issued last summer as a revision of our strategic nuclear doctrine. According to some Carter Administration officials, Presidential Directive 59 was intended to get away from reliance on deterrence alone and to reshape our targeting policy so that we might engage with the Soviets in a controlled and protracted exchange of strategic nuclear weapons — a kind of mutual destruction in neat, tidy stages.

This re-emergence of the conceits of the early 1950s that nuclear weapons are just another form of armament, to be employed rationally to advance our national interests, tragically confirms Albert Einstein's observation: "The unleashed power of the atom has changed everything — except our way of thinking."

Mr. Goodwin's book is a powerful plea for reason. Faced with the facts about nuclear destruction, reason must tell us that anything that moves us closer to that disaster, like a limited nuclear war-fighting strategy, is unambiguously bad. It must also tell us that anything that lessens the mortal danger, like the restrictions in the SALT II treaty, is unambiguously good. And an enlightened public can take the political profit out of being wrong on the most important issue of our time.

Paul C. Warnke

1 Taking the threat seriously

Nine Americans out of every ten could perish in an all-out nuclear attack against the United States. Not all of these would die instantly: many deaths would be delayed for hours, days or weeks before injuries, severe burns and radiation sickness took their toll. In the following months epidemics of disease (worsened by an almost complete lack of medical facilities), starvation and the breakdown of law and order could kill yet more citizens.

This prospect is substantially the same for any country attacked. Any country which is the theatre of a nuclear war could be bombarded with enough nuclear explosions to be devastated several times over, with vast areas made lethally radioactive for a period of several months. Not even the sophisticated Swiss civil defence programme, which includes blast shelters for nearly everybody and even underground hospitals, is capable of protecting all citizens for months on end, or allows for the restructuring of agriculture and industry to take sufficient account in the long term of dangerous fallout as well as blast and fire destruction. Even areas not directly involved in any conflict could suffer from the catastrophic effects of fallout and huge economic, social and political problems.

In any country which suffered an attack by nuclear weapons, many people would die as a result of the strike. Of those who survived, only a small minority would have done so because they knew what to do, or because they had made advance preparation: the majority would survive *by chance*. The numbers who died or who survived would depend almost entirely on the targeting policy of the nation mounting the attack, a factor over which one could have no control. Those who survived because of the preparations they had made would be sheltering on the fringes of areas of blast devastation or from radioactive fallout. With knowledge, luck, intelligence, strong will and the ability to overcome fear and panic, such people might exercise survival skills successfully. But the majority of any population under attack would never be in a position to benefit from such skills.

It has been argued that the results of an attack could be so appalling that nuclear war would never be allowed to happen. But if this were true no government would talk about the 'nuclear deterrent'. If nuclear weapons are used to deter war we have to believe that they would be used if the circumstances became sufficiently serious: deterrence cannot work if everybody agrees that the weapons are too dangerous to use. Clearly many governments do not consider them too dangerous because today we rely heavily on these weapons' deterrent value to preserve peace. Deterrence appears to work very well indeed. But to be acceptable to present and future generations 'very well indeed' is not enough.

Deterrence policies have led to a build-up of arms intended to produce the desired balance of terror between potentially opposing forces: Warsaw Pact and NATO, the United States and the USSR, China and Russia, and other candidate nuclear opponents. But the dangers have become magnified enormously by 'overkill': the capacity

Hiroshima was flattened and gutted by a weapon which today would be classed as a 'low-yield' nuclear bomb.

to have enough undamaged warheads after an attack to mount a retaliatory nuclear strike which would cause unacceptable damage to the enemy. Overkill requires that the United States and the Soviet Union possess far more nuclear weapons than would be necessary to destroy each other.

It is calculated that in a conflict between the two major nuclear powers a surprise attack could eliminate 90 per cent of the land-based ballistic missiles possessed by the nation under attack.[1] Yet it would leave the country attacked with enough warheads to cause an unacceptable amount of damage in retaliation. Similar calculations can be made for other nuclear weapon delivery systems. Overkill also takes account of the fact that missiles might miss their targets or might not work (today's nuclear weapons have not been tested under true conditions

of war), so the huge number of weapons in existence today (possibly 50,000 or more[2]) are considered necessary by the nuclear powers to achieve effective, credible deterrence. Needless to say, overkill has introduced bigger dangers if deterrence breaks down.

The military justification for overkill has grown up alongside the suggestion that nuclear war could be limited (the 'counterforce' war against nuclear weapons' delivery systems and bases being a particularly favoured choice of limited nuclear attack strategy). But the opposing view was summed up by Professor Wolfgang Panofsky of Stanford University who, in January 1981, told a meeting of French, Russian and American scientists and armaments experts in Paris:

'A nuclear weapon which misses its assigned target still does an enormous amount of damage ... Once nuclear war is initiated by any power, under any doctrine, in any theatre, or for any strategic or tactical purpose, the outcome will involve truly massive casualties and devastation, leading to incalculable effects on the future of mankind.'

Dire warnings of the consequences of nuclear war were also given recently in a meticulously researched report from the US Office of Technology Assessment, *The Effects of Nuclear War*. The authors point out that above all it should be remembered that nuclear weapon effects are uncertain, but they add that, 'Throughout all the variations, possibilities and uncertainties ... one theme is constant: that nuclear war would be a catastrophe.'[3]

This is, of course, no more than we should expect. After all we have been paying scientists and engineers to devise and develop effective nuclear weapon systems for many years. It is not surprising that more than a generation after the Hiroshima explosion they have achieved the ability to annihilate entire continents: we are simply getting a proper return on our investment. Politically

Gigantic B-52 bombers can fly at roof-top height but might still not survive to reach their targets within the Soviet Union.

and militarily, the return seems to be more effective deterrence. If the weapons were used, however, the effect on the world could be even more serious and far reaching than is suggested by merely calculating likely levels of devastation in different places. Our planet might not be big enough to absorb nuclear punishment: the world is like an organic entity, with its constituent parts, countries and continents, intimately dependent upon one another. Nuclear devastation in one part of the world, however 'limited', could have permanent consequences for the whole planet.

When the United States first deployed nuclear weapons in the 1950s these assured deterrence because the Soviet Union did not have any. But as soon as Russia developed an equivalent arsenal a nuclear stalemate was produced, which hung on the threat of 'mutual assured destruction' (MAD for short). This continued until the late 1970s: it deterred nuclear war because neither side could use nuclear weapons without risking devastation to both. Overkill capacities made the MAD relationship yet more dangerous and war unthinkable. This is now changing, however, as a range of 'credible' nuclear war-fighting strategies are being considered. The limited counterforce attack is one of them.

Both superpowers accepted MAD until recently because their nuclear war-fighting abilities were too primitive. They did not have sufficient confidence that their weapons could successfully attack protected missile silos. Because these are 'hardened' against nuclear weapon effects by thicknesses of reinforced concrete they can only be destroyed by direct hits or very close strikes. Missile guidance systems have now improved sufficiently to raise the chances of a successful strike to a high degree, at least in theory.[4] Another uncertainty which seems to have been resolved is warhead reliability and readiness for use. Far greater confidence exists among the military that their weapons would work properly if the order were given. And with massive numbers of warheads available, making it possible to attack each hardened silo with two weapons, there is a much greater chance of

Frequent testing of 'devices' (above, Bikini in 1956) adds impetus to the arms race.

a 'kill'. The ability to retaliate to a limited counterforce attack might thus be greatly reduced.

These same factors of improved accuracy and reliability also give a massive advantage to any side willing to make the first strike: a timely decision to execute a limited counterforce strike against missiles and perhaps also bomber and submarine bases would offer the hope of limiting the damage by retaliation even though some weapons would inevitably survive. If the political situation became sufficiently grave it is conceivable that a national leader might consider the damage by retaliation worth the risk.

NATO threatens the first use of nuclear weapons in Europe if it cannot repulse any possible Soviet aggression in western Europe by other means. If the Soviet Union became absolutely convinced that NATO was about to use nuclear weapons it is conceivable that it would strike first to avoid suffering even more damage by failing to eliminate as many NATO nuclear weapons as possible. A game of political and strategic brinkmanship is in progress which makes nuclear war continually possible. Ironically it is this game of 'dare' which also makes deterrence work, but undoubtedly it also gives the advantage to whichever side strikes first.

Other technological developments make nuclear war-fighting more credible and a 'first strike' more likely in extreme circumstances. Radio and satellite links now make it possible for submarines to fix their positions at sea more accurately than ever before, so they can point their missiles more precisely at small, hardened missile silos and not just large civilian targets. According to the Stockholm International Peace Research Institute (SIPRI), submarine detection systems such as sonar and satellite surveillance might soon make the oceans' 'transparent' so that submarines could be more easily detected and destroyed by a pre-emptive strike.[5] If this is true, they would be useful only for 'first strike' use. They would be sitting ducks after the beginning of a nuclear war and might not survive to take part in retaliation. It would also be relatively easy to destroy the Very Low Frequency (VLF) radio transmitting masts used for communicating with missile-carrying submarines.

Anti-ballistic missile systems (ABMs) could either increase stability in nuclear deterrence or reduce it drastically. The recently proposed 'laser anti-ballistic missile system' would consist of a device mounted on a satellite which could point a powerful laser beam at a ballistic missile in flight. The heat energy generated by the laser beam would cause enough damage either to prevent the warhead from detonating properly or to stop the missile carrying it re-entering the earth's atmosphere. If both the United States and the Soviet Union possessed such systems neither would be able to strike the other with intercontinental ballistic missiles, so strategic nuclear war could be made a great deal more difficult. But if one side launched a laser ABM before the other, it could prevent the other launching its own. The first side with laser ABMs in orbit would be able to threaten nuclear destruction without any fear of retaliation.

It can be argued that because missiles are now more accurate and reliable, because war-fighting strategies could be credible, there could be a degree of agreement between politicians, the military and the public that under extreme provocation nuclear weapons should be used. It is known that areas of population need not be deliberately targeted, so the prospect of war – though still abhorrent – might become more acceptable than it was in the days of mutual assured destruction. But a limited counterforce attack against a superpower could nevertheless involve the loss of 20 million Russian or American lives.

Although a surprise attack cannot be completely ruled out it is far more likely that only after a conventional war would nuclear weapons be used, followed by escalation if the initial attack did not end the war. In Europe the 'flexible response' policy of NATO makes exactly this possible. It is assumed that deterrence is far more effective if a range of 'levels' of escalation are available for use as increasing threats. In the event of an overwhelming Russian attack, small numbers of tactical (usually short range) weapons would be tried first, followed by larger numbers (provided they survived enemy retaliation) if the first salvo did not lead to surrender. The NATO theory is that the Soviet Union could surrender after any of the levels of nuclear attack, and, it is hoped, before a full scale war developed between the superpowers.

The USSR and NATO believe they have tuned the balance of terror so finely in Europe that war is deterred. Pessimists say that tactical weapons are of 'questionable survivability' and might all be destroyed before they could be used either for attack or deterrence. With tens of thousands of warheads on each side in Europe it is hard to assure the person in the street (particularly the German street) that one day things will not go wrong.

Today many countries have the ability to make nuclear bombs – there are not simply the two American- and Russian-dominated sides to bring into the calculations. To complicate matters, Britain has a partially independent and France and China fully independent nuclear capabilities; India now also has the bomb; Pakistan is thought to be building the first 'Islamic H-bomb'; South Africa is suspected to be developing nuclear weapons, and Israel might have a nuclear arsenal almost poised for attack. Other countries possessing nuclear reactors have the technical capability and the raw materials for producing them. The use of nuclear power for generating electricity has led to the setting up of hundreds of nuclear reactors all over the world. Each reactor generates not only electricity but also creates plutonium, a material which when refined and separated from the other reactor wastes can be made into bomb material. It seems inconceivable that nuclear power stations all over the world will become outlawed and shut down. The 'energy crisis' seems to demand that more, not less, nuclear power should be used in the future. This implies the production of more plutonium and an ever-rising capacity for global destruction.

The peaceful use of nuclear power is not restricted by international agreement. The build-up of weapons systems is not seriously hindered by international agreements such as those resulting from the Strategic Arms Limitations Talks (SALT), though such agreements as have been reached are to be welcomed. Unless powerful international controls restricting the production, testing, deployment and use of nuclear weapons are introduced we cannot be assured that the risk of nuclear war is reduced. As long as nuclear arsenals exist there can be no guarantee that the weapons will never be used.

So the possibility of nuclear war cannot be dismissed. While wars continue in many parts of the globe and tension between the superpowers waxes and wanes, as the world fights recession and other seemingly insoluble problems many people now believe that nuclear war could happen, if not in their

'Many were killed instantly, others lay writhing on the ground screaming in agony from the intolerable pain of their burns. Everything . . . was annihilated . . . Hiroshima had ceased to exist.'[6]

lifetime then in the lifetimes of their children. If so, there is much to be said for making preparations: by understanding nuclear weapon effects it is conceivable that a small number of individuals might help preserve their own lives if the worst comes to the worst.

A lot of publicity is given to civil defence and sheltering as a means of protecting populations from the effects of nuclear war. Although adequate shelters could protect people in the short term from nuclear attack there could be no guarantee about the long-term future. Evacuation, either to a different continent or within a country, would also offer some level of protection from immediate effects of nuclear bombardment. But no country could escape economic, social and other repercussions which might arise in the wake of a large-scale nuclear conflict. Neither could any country necessarily escape long-term fallout. If sufficient weapon power were unleashed the global fallout could produce epidemics of cancer and birth defects in peoples anywhere in the world, not to mention its effects on other animals and crops. Fallout alone could strike a blow from which civilisation might never recover.

It would be a mistake to think that self protection and civil defence provide the sole answer. Nuclear war *must* be prevented. The future must be safeguarded by getting rid of the policy of deterrence and preserving world peace by some other, less risky, method. As long as we continue to rely on the balance of terror produced by nuclear arsenals we shall never be free from the inescapable risk that something will go wrong. A small risk endured for a sufficiently long time brings the certainty that the risk will be fulfilled: an alternative to nuclear deterrence must be found if present and future generations are to be guaranteed a chance of survival.

2 Nuclear weapons and their effects

Make no mistake about it, nuclear bombs are quite totally different from any other form of weapon. To begin with, their explosive power can be millions of times greater than the biggest conventional (high explosive) bombs; to add to this destructive capability they also generate dangerous radiation which could kill and maim even more victims than the stupendous blast and heat which is produced.

The bomb which destroyed Hiroshima in 1945 was a comparatively modest nuclear weapon by today's standards. Nevertheless it killed 80,000 people – more than the number killed by bombs in Great Britain during the whole of the Second World War. Many survivors of the Hiroshima blast died later from injuries, burns and infections, their bodies weakened by radiation which, in some, caused fatal illnesses such as leukaemia years later.

In the shorthand jargon of nuclear weaponry the Hiroshima bomb was rated as a 12.5 kiloton (or kt) weapon, ie it was equivalent to 12,500 tons of TNT high explosive. Many present-day weapons have explosive powers of several megatons (or Mt) – equivalent to several *million* tons of TNT. The most powerful bomb ever known to have been exploded (experimentally) was over 50 megatons in yield.[1] To say that nuclear bombs are millions of times more powerful than conventional bombs, however, is still not enough to convey their dreadful effects, for the huge concentration of energy within the nuclear fireball created at the point of explosion has other lethal effects.

Converting matter into energy

Until the twentieth century it was thought that matter could neither be created nor destroyed. The same was thought to be true of energy. But Albert Einstein realised that it is possible under special circumstances to convert matter into energy, or energy into matter. Normally this never happens, but when scientists started to experiment with atoms they proved that matter from the innermost parts of the atom *could* be converted into energy, and a huge new source of power could be tapped. When the Second World War began, it became a matter of urgency to develop bombs which derive energy from splitting the atom.

Nuclear bombs

There are two basic types of nuclear bomb. In the first, called a 'fission' or atom bomb, atoms are split apart. This can only happen to very large atoms such as those of the element uranium. The nucleus breaks up into two smaller pieces and several neutrons, releasing energy while the disintegration takes place.

The hydrogen or 'fusion' bomb, works by fusing atoms of light elements together – particularly hydrogen, which then forms helium. This process also releases large amounts of energy by the destruction of matter within the nucleus.

Nuclear fission

The heaviest element found in nature, uranium, has 92 protons within the nucleus of every atom. But there are several different isotopes of uranium. More than 99 per

The Atom

Everything is made from atoms. Our bodies consist of millions of them joined together in a complex way to form the entire human organism. Atoms are so small that they cannot normally be seen at all. Not all atoms are the same, however, and there is a slight variation in size between those of different elements.

Each atom consists of a tiny central kernel called the nucleus surrounded by a cloud of electrically-charged particles called electrons which circle the nucleus. Each electron carries one single unit called the 'electron charge' of negative electricity. The electron cloud makes up most of the atom's size, but it weighs several thousand times less than the nucleus. The nucleus is so much smaller than the electron cloud that about 100,000 nuclei could stand side-by-side within the width of a single electron cloud.

It has been found that nuclei themselves are built up from at least two simpler 'building blocks': the proton and the neutron. (Ordinary hydrogen is the one exception to this having no neutron.) Each of these blocks weighs about 2,000 times as much as an electron.

Protons carry one positive charge of electricity each, equal and opposite to the negative charge carried by each electron.

Neutrons, although about the same weight as protons, carry no electric charge at all, although it is sometimes possible for a neutron to disintegrate within the nucleus and form a proton and an electron. The latter shoots out from the nucleus at great speed and is then called a beta particle.

The distinguishing feature which makes atoms of one element quite different from those of another is the number of proton particles within the nucleus.

Isotopes: Each atom of an element has the same number of protons in its nucleus, but the neutrons can vary. These variants are called 'isotopes'. Hydrogen, for instance, can exist as three different isotopes: each has a single proton, but ordinary hydrogen has no neutron, hydrogen 2 (also called deuterium) has one neutron in the nucleus and hydrogen 3 (tritium) has two neutrons. Chemically all isotopes of the same element behave in the same way, but the different contents of the nuclei make big differences to their behaviour in nuclear reactions.

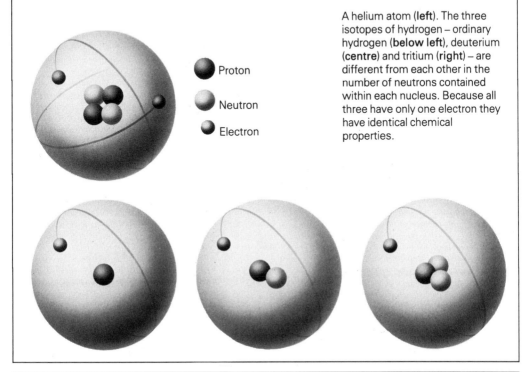

Proton

Neutron

Electron

A helium atom (**left**). The three isotopes of hydrogen – ordinary hydrogen (**below left**), deuterium (**centre**) and tritium (**right**) – are different from each other in the number of neutrons contained within each nucleus. Because all three have only one electron they have identical chemical properties.

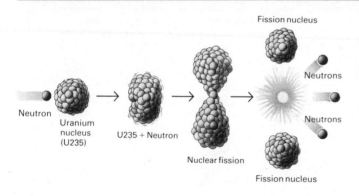

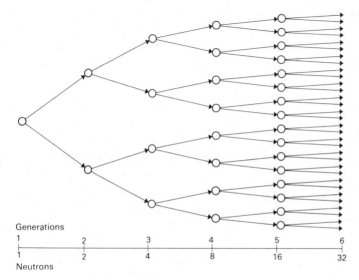

When a single nucleus of uranium 235 (**left**) splits up during the process of fission it releases neutrons in addition to the two unequal fragments. This makes the chain reaction (**below**) possible. Normally at least two neutrons are produced by each fissioning uranium nucleus. These fly off and if conditions are favourable can cause fission in more uranium nuclei which would not have split had they not been disturbed by the arrival of the high-speed neutrons. Thus, under ideal conditions, it is possible for the first generation of one fissioning nucleus to cause a second generation of at least two uranium nuclei to split up, which in turn could cause a third generation and so on. In this way each generation could double the number of nuclei splitting up and releasing their nuclear energy. In practice the explosive chain reaction would happen in less than a millionth of a second, though not all uranium nuclei would fission (some would not absorb neutrons).

cent of the natural element consists of uranium 238, which has 146 neutrons in the nucleus together with the 92 protons. Nearly all the remaining natural uranium consists of isotope 235, which has only 143 neutrons in each nucleus. This difference turns out to be vital because neutrons are involved in the processes by which the nucleus is held together and prevented, under normal circumstances, from disintegrating. A few neutrons added to or subtracted from a nucleus can make a great deal of difference to an element's stability.

Uranium 235 is less stable than uranium 238; in a lump of uranium 235 containing millions of atoms, a few disintegrate spontaneously at any one moment. Each nucleus splits, or fissions, into two smaller parts forming different elements. When fission takes place neutrons are also released from the nucleus together with pure energy in the form of gamma rays.

Because each fissioning nucleus releases neutrons, these in turn can cause fission in other uranium 235 nuclei nearby. A chain of fission reactions can occur if there are enough fissionable nuclei in the vicinity (a 'critical' amount). If the chain reaction is allowed to proceed an explosion can take place in a tiny fraction of a second. This is what happens in a fission bomb.

The smallest amount of fissionable material needed to produce a chain reaction is called the critical mass. A few pounds of uranium 235 can form a critical mass. If compressed by an explosion – one of the means by which some bombs are triggered – even smaller amounts can become critical. This is because the nuclei are much closer together than in the uncompressed state. An alternative means of detonation is suddenly to bring together two pieces of uranium which are each individually less than the critical mass but which equal or just exceed this amount when brought into contact.

Heavier elements than uranium can be produced artificially. Uranium 238 absorbs neutrons inside nuclear reactors, becoming a different isotope – uranium 239. This is not stable, but releases two electrons (beta particles) from the nucleus. The residue forms the element plutonium, which then has 94 protons in each nucleus as a result of two neutrons within the nucleus being converted into protons by the release of the two beta particles. All nuclear reactors produce plutonium as a by-product. Like uranium 235, plutonium is also fissionable and works very well in fission bombs. Since it is more readily obtainable than uranium 235, it is of immense importance in the making of nuclear weapons.

Fusion bomb
When nuclei of the lightest element, hydrogen, are fused together to form nuclei of helium, matter is converted into energy and, as in the fission of uranium or plutonium, a great deal of energy is released. The hydrogen isotopes deuterium and tritium react with each other to produce the most energy of all the fusion reactions.

The fusion reaction will only begin, however, if the temperature of the mixture of hydrogen isotopes is raised to tens of millions of degrees centigrade. To do this, a fission bomb is used as a trigger for the fusion bomb. Hence fusion bombs always combine fission with fusion.

Hydrogen (fusion) bombs can be more powerful than a simple fission bomb because fusion of a mixture of deuterium and tritium can produce nearly three times as much energy as fission of the same weight of uranium or plutonium. In addition, however, large amounts of deuterium and tritium can be stored in the bomb before detonation without any risk of the mass becoming critical, whereas in a pure fission bomb it is difficult to keep large quantities of material sufficiently separated to prevent the chain reaction from starting.

Fission bomb
Trigger (1) ignites TNT charge (2) propelling sub-critical masses (3) into each other to form super-critical assembly of fissionable material.

Fission-fusion bomb
As before, but (4) consists of the tritium/deuterium 'fusion' mixture instead of being a non-reactive casing or neutron reflector.

Fission-fusion-fission bomb
As for fission-fusion, but the outer casing (5) consists of uranium 238 (covered by a protective skin) which fissions when triggered by the fusion explosion.

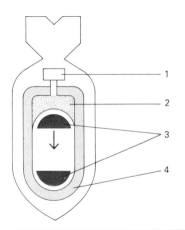

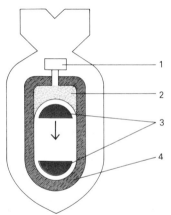

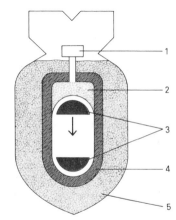

Delivery systems

Nuclear warheads can be delivered to their targets by means of shells, bombs or missiles. They can be fired from silos, aircraft, submarines and even huge guns. A distinction is sometimes drawn between 'strategic', 'theatre', and 'tactical' nuclear weapons. It is approximately true to say that strategic weapons are those which can be delivered to a very distant target, one in another continent, whereas tactical weapons are for exactly the opposite purpose: for fighting battles between armies. Normally tactical weapons have much shorter ranges, from hundreds down to only a few miles, and have lower yields.

Theatre weapons are intermediate in range: they are intended for fighting a campaign in a particular region, or theatre, of the world in a war which does not spread across the globe. Although intermediate in range between strategic and tactical weapons, they are not necessarily intermediate in explosive yield: some are just as powerful as the strategic weapons. (The words 'theatre' and 'tactical' are often used interchangeably.)

Although a clear distinction cannot truly be made between these different categories, strategic arms are the only ones strictly limited by international agreement. The Strategic Arms Limitation Talks (SALT) between the Soviet Union and the United States have limited the number of weapons described as strategic, but have not controlled theatre or tactical arsenals.[2]

Ballistic missiles

The ballistic missile has transformed the nature of war because of its great speed. It consists fundamentally of one or more warheads mounted on a space rocket. Because the rocket is shot out of the earth's atmosphere it can accelerate to about 15,000 miles per hour (24,000 km/h) without having to push against the air which at lower altitudes would make such a high speed impossible. So strategic missiles can fly between continents in about 20 minutes. Theatre missiles can reach targets several miles away in just a few minutes.

Accuracy

The word ballistic implies that the missile is 'thrown' to its target. The rocket motors only operate for the first acceleration, which takes the missile out of the atmosphere. After that it simply flies like a bullet, a method needing considerable accuracy. This is provided by computers (on the ground and in the rocket) connected to 'inertial navigation systems' – devices such as gyro-compasses – linked electronically so as to detect every acceleration the rocket makes and thus to keep track of its precise location. While the rocket motors are still burning, the inertial navigation system establishes whether the missile is on course and makes any adjustments necessary to improve the accuracy of its flightpath.

Despite tremendous navigational advances, doubts are still raised about the targeting accuracy of ballistic missiles. Areas of improvement in missile guidance systems are, understandably, closely guarded military secrets, but it is known that mid-flight correction could be made, for instance, by mounting a telescope on the missile capable of taking a 'fix' from one or more stars.[3] So-called 'terminal guidance' (for recognising the individual target and correcting the missile flightpath yet again to bring the warhead on to it) could be achieved by a number of possible methods such as radar capable of recognising terrain in the target zone. But all of these methods are fraught with difficulties.[4]

Because a missile can only be expected to have a chance, not a certainty, of striking the target, estimates of the accuracy of any particular system result in a figure called the circular error probable, or CEP. This is the radius of a circle (the centre of which is the target) within which half of the missiles targeted are likely to fall. Even when missile systems are thought to have quite small CEPs[5] no claims are made about the likely landing sites of the 50 per cent of warheads which fall outside the CEP radius so that you could expect some missiles to land off course, introducing yet more uncertainty into any actual nuclear conflict.

The Pershing 1A short-range ballistic missile carries a more powerful warhead than the Hiroshima bomb distances of up to 435 miles (700 kilometres). The 180 NATO Pershing 1As based in Europe are designed for 'limited' battlefield fighting in which the devastation is restricted. (The new Pershing 2 missile, however, is totally different, being capable of reaching the Soviet Union from its proposed West German bases.)

The Lance tactical short-range ballistic missile has a range of only 63 miles (100 km) but explodes with a force almost as great as the Hiroshima bomb. A small number of the hundreds of such 'tactical weapons' deployed by NATO might be used in the opening stages of the Third World War. More than one thousand similar warheads based in East Europe are poised for the reply.

Pluton (**above**) is France's independent short-range ballistic missile, carrying either a 10-kt or 25-kt warhead. (The smaller warhead is said to be needed for 'close' fighting, but is sufficient to destroy a large town.) The Soviet Union includes the SS-1 'Scud' missile (**left**) in its armoury of 'tactical' weapons comparable with Pluton and Lance.

If armies came within ten miles of each other, 1-kt shells shot from NATO's M-110 howitzer guns (**below**) and their Soviet equivalent, the S-23, might fly in large numbers.

Cruise missiles are small, pilotless aircraft which can be equipped with high-yield nuclear warheads. The Boeing cruise missile (**above** and **right**) can fly long distances at very low altitude – below 300 feet (100 m) and can locate its target with pin-point accuracy (by scanning an electronic 'map' of the target area). The Soviet Union deploys cruise missiles launched from aircraft, submarines and ground bases. America plans to equip B-52 bombers with up to 20 air-launched cruise missiles (ALCMs) each and to base ground-launched cruise missiles (GLCMs) widely through Europe.

Doubts are voiced about the aircraft's 'survivability' however, because it flies at less than the speed of sound, might easily be detected by enemy radar and shot down. One big advantage is that they are 'cheap', costing less than 1 million dollars each compared with, for example, billions of dollars for the proposed MX American land-based missile system. Critics suggest however that they merely act as targets which would be attacked in the opening stages of a nuclear war, and discount their ability to penetrate enemy defences.

The Tu-95 'Bear' (**above**) can fly 8,000 miles (13,000 kilometres) without refuelling, and together with the 'Bison' is capable of delivering high-yield nuclear bombs accurately on to American targets. This Soviet threat is countered by the B-52 long-range bomber (**below**) of America's Strategic Air Command, supported by Britain's medium-range Vulcan bomber (**left**) which is also able to threaten targets on Soviet soil.

The Polaris missile (**right**) launched from a submerged submarine, can deliver its three 200-kt warheads to three separate targets. The Trident C4, (**above**) carrying eight 100-kt warheads, is the latest American submarine-launched ballistic missile (SLBM).

The targeting accuracy of SLBMs is disputed: some say that such missiles are now accurate enough to be used against protected missile silos; others say that only 'soft' targets such as factories and airfields could be attacked, putting large numbers of civilians at risk from immediate bomb effects.

Sea-bottom sonar arrays (**below**) are used in an attempt to detect submerged submarines. Northern Hemisphere seas are dotted with these devices (the probable maximum surveillance areas are shaded).

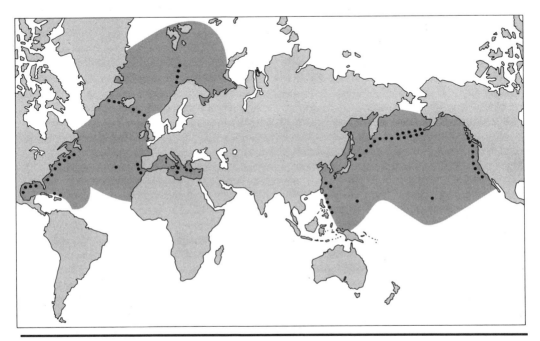

Electronic guidance makes anti-aircraft systems such as the surface-to-air missiles (**above**) deadly accurate giving aircraft and cruise missiles little or no chance of penetrating the defences.

Fylingdales Early Warning Station (**below left**) in Yorkshire, England, is one of a network of radar systems designed to give at least a few minutes' warning of missile attack.

The 'Maverick' homing missile, (**below right**) can seek a tank by detecting infra-red (heat) energy produced by the engine, even in fog or dark.

The proposed American MX underground mobile missile system is designed to protect land-based missiles against nuclear attack – each 'race track' (1) protects a missile which moves from one hardened shelter (2) to another in a transporter/launcher (3). By making the precise locations of missiles uncertain the system guarantees a greater capacity for retaliation.

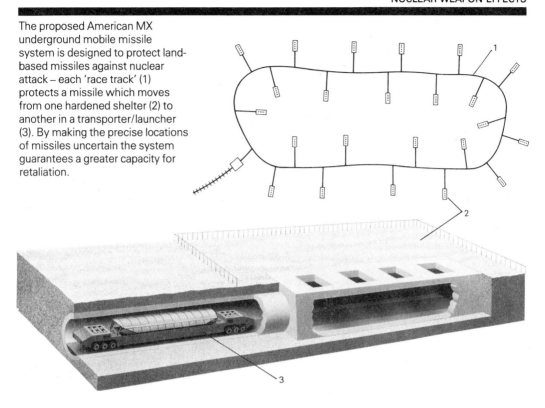

The Neutron Bomb

The neutron bomb is basically a very small hydrogen (fission-fusion) bomb, producing as much of its energy as possible in the form of neutrons. Such a weapon kills people by a slow lingering death from radiation sickness, but it can be detonated far enough above buildings to cause relatively little damage by blast and heat, even though the explosion is no less powerful than many of the small bombs classed as tactical weapons.

The required effect could be produced by using about an ounce of fissionable material (triggered by compression using a TNT charge) which then ignites a similar amount of tritium/deuterium fusion mixture.

Because so little fissionable material is used the weapon is fairly 'clean', releasing only small quantities of fission products: ideal if the area being attacked by the bomb is to be used by invading forces. The initial neutron radiation delivers its deadly dose in seconds leaving little fallout – provided the weapon is air burst as it must be to reduce or avoid property damage.

For military purposes, however, the neutron bomb has severe drawbacks: it does not kill like a shower of bullets. Soldiers receiving far more than a lethal dose of neutrons would be able to continue to fight for several hours or days, so there are serious questions about the military value of neutron bombs.

It is not often realised that NATO's proposal to deploy the neutron bomb in Europe was because it seemed to solve the problem posed by tactical weapons: that of their own arsenals causing massive destruction to their own territory, such as West Germany, if nuclear weapons were ever used in any attempt to stem Warsaw Pact aggression. The West Germans have never been very enthusiastic about it, however.

Nobody has yet devised a weapon with a truly intermediate explosive yield: between that of nuclear and conventional weapons. Even the neutron bomb must inevitably create a very powerful nuclear explosion, and its ideal of killing people without damaging property would, in practice, be very difficult to realise.

The nuclear explosion

The nuclear fireball is as hot as the sun, indeed its immense power is derived from nuclear reactions similar to those happening continuously within the sun. The very high temperatures cause a blinding flash of light and heat to radiate out from the explosion. Anyone looking at the fireball could be blinded for several minutes or hours, or severely damage their eyes. Within a few miles from the explosion exposed skin and flesh might be charred and burnt from the bone and houses could burst into flames. A whole city could ignite within seconds and might even become engulfed in a 'fire storm' – a raging inferno which sucks in air from the surrounding area and would not abate until everything was burnt.

When the bomb is exploded in the atmosphere, the fireball is almost spherical. In less than a thousandth of a second after detonation, the fireball from a 1-Mt explosion grows to more than 300 feet (100 metres) wide, and is nearly 6,000 feet (2 km) wide after ten seconds. [6] At the same time, it rises like a hot-air balloon, at about 300 feet every second.

Air bursts and surface bursts

If the fireball does not touch the ground (detonation having taken place in the atmosphere) the explosion is described as an air burst. For a 1-Mt bomb, for example, the explosive point would have to be more than half a mile (1 km) above the ground to be classed as an air burst – higher than the greatest radius of the fireball.

When the height of an explosion is greater than about 100,000 feet (30 km) it is called a high altitude explosion, being above most of the earth's atmosphere. The effects on the ground would then be different from lower bursts within the atmosphere.

Detonation on the ground, or close enough for the fireball to touch the surface, is called a surface burst.

Heat effects

About one-third of the nuclear fireball's energy is radiated as intense heat. In clear weather the heat flash could instantly set fire to objects and harm people.

Air bursts can cause greater heat damage

The mushroom cloud is the result of heat released. The fireball rises leaving behind a partial vacuum into which air flows from the surroundings (**above**). In an air burst (**centre**) the fireball does not touch the ground. A surface burst (**right**) creates a crater.

than ground bursts because the heat rays can travel further without getting absorbed by buildings, hills and other surface features. The more powerful the weapon, the longer the pulse of heat (over three seconds for a 20-Mt weapon, compared with one-fifth of a second for 25-kt). Most substances would be less likely to be damaged by a particular amount of heat if it were spread out over several seconds than they would be if it were delivered in one sudden flash. Calculations show that within a range called the fire zone, most combustible materials would be ignited in clear, dry weather.

Eye damage

A brief, direct glimpse of the fireball could cause temporary blindness lasting from a few minutes to some hours (called flash-blindness) or permanent eye damage (retinal burns) which could impair vision, though not necessarily cause total blindness. A 100-kt weapon exploding at a height of 50,000 feet (15.2 km) could cause flash-blindness even in daytime (when the eye is adapted to bright light) at a distance of over 20 miles (32 km). The same explosion would cause retinal burns at a distance of 27 miles (43.2 km) in daytime, and at more than 70 miles (112 km) distance at night (when the iris is dilated to improve vision in low-light conditions).

Air blast

The enormous pressure which builds up within a fraction of a second at the point of explosion is the source of a high-pressure blast wave, capable of striking property and people like a giant hammer blow. The blast wave travels outwards from the centre of the explosion at approximately the speed of sound (1,100 feet per second/330 metres per second), so it takes about five seconds to travel 1 mile (three seconds to travel 1 km). When an explosion occurs the first effect is the blinding flash of light, accompanied by an invisible 'flash' of radiation (which would be lethal if you were close enough). But there is no noise until the blast wave arrives, just as thunder follows lightning.

If you could count the seconds between the light flash and the arrival of the blast wave you might estimate your distance from the point of detonation. Knowing this distance could help you to survive in some circumstances.

Drag effects

The blast wave pushes air bodily outwards from the point of the explosion causing tremendously strong winds. Although the blast pressure could crush huge buildings, as much damage might be caused by loose objects (such as cars, trucks, people and flying debris) being blown by the hurricane-force winds. Winds from a 20-Mt bomb exploded over Kennedy Airport could reach 200 miles per hour (320 km/h) on the East Side of Manhattan. Survival would be practically impossible for anybody caught out in the open; people indoors would probably be trapped beneath tons of fallen masonry.

Afterwinds

Following the initial outward rush of wind accompanying the blast wave, a gentler afterwind blows back inwards towards the point of explosion. This is not likely to be dangerous in most circumstances.

How blast damages buildings

Before the blast wave arrives the pressure over the building is normal atmospheric: 14.7 pounds per square inch (psi). The blast wave itself consists of an advancing 'slice' of air which is compressed to over normal atmospheric pressure, a so-called 'overpressure'. Not only does a wave of compression move outwards from the explosive point, but air also moves itself, causing very strong winds. So there are two kinds of pressures exerted suddenly on buildings in the path of this blast wave: the sudden overpressure and the drag pressure caused by the wind.

Vertical walls, particularly those directly facing the on-coming blast wave (ie towards the explosive point) reflect the overpressure blast wave like a racket reflecting a tennis ball back down the court. A force of twice the overpressure is felt on the side of a building because of this reflection. But when the wind drag effects are added the

Blast effects of air-burst weapons at optimum altitude for range indicated*

Distance from explosion		1-kt weapon	150-kt weapon
1 mile	overpressure winds	1.4 psi 50 mph cuts and blows from flying debris many buildings moderately damaged	18 psi 420 mph humans battered to death heavy machinery such as locomotives dragged reinforced concrete building severely damaged
2 miles	overpressure winds	0.5 psi below 35 mph many broken windows	6 psi 190 mph some eardrums ruptured bones fractured houses destroyed all trees blown down telephone lines dragged severely
5 miles	overpressure winds		1.5 psi 55 mph cuts and blows from flying debris many buildings moderately damaged
10 miles	overpressure winds		0.6 psi below 35 mph many broken windows
20 miles	overpressure winds		
40 miles	overpressure winds		

* The range of effects required dictates the explosion's optimum height.

Source: Calculated from the 'Nuclear Bomb Effects Computer' in Glasstone, Samuel and Dolan, Philip J., *The Effects of Nuclear Weapons*, 3rd ed.

total reflected pressure can rise to much more than twice the blast overpressure. If the blast wave does not squash the building flat, therefore, the 'hammer blow' of such reflection effects could demolish a wall.

There are several different ways in which the unequal distribution of pressure can crush a building. If not many doors and windows were open it might simply be crushed flat because the pressure outside was much greater than that inside. If they were strong enough, however, the sides and roof not facing the blast might withstand the maximum overpressure, but the wall

1-Mt weapon	10-Mt weapon	20-Mt weapon
43 psi 1,700 mph many humans killed	above 200 psi above 2,000 mph buried 8-inch thick concrete arch destroyed	greatly above 200 psi greatly above 2,000 mph total destruction

17 psi
400 mph
humans battered to death
lung haemorrhage
eardrums ruptured
heavy machinery dragged
   severely (such as loco-
   motives)
	50 psi
	1,800 mph
	humans fatally crushed
	severe damage to buried light
	   corrugated steel arch
		84 psi
		2,000 mph
		lethal zone
		buried steel structures
		   destroyed

4 psi
130 mph
bones fractured
90% trees down
many buildings flattened
	14 psi
	330 mph
	eardrums ruptured
	lung haemorrhage
	reinforced concrete building
	   severely damaged
		19 psi
		440 mph
		humans battered to death
		lung haemorrhage
		eardrums ruptured
		reinforced concrete building
		   destroyed

1.4 psi
50 mph
cuts and blows from flying
   debris
many buildings moderately
   damaged
	4.4 psi
	150 mph
	bones fractured
	90% trees down
	many buildings flattened
		6 psi
		200 mph
		some eardrums ruptured
		bones fractured
		houses destroyed
		all trees blown down
		telephone lines dragged
		   severely

below 1 psi
below 35 mph
many broken windows
	1.5 psi
	55 mph
	cuts and blows from flying
	   debris
	many buildings moderately
	   damaged
		2.3 psi
		75 mph
		blows and deep cuts from flying
		   debris
		many houses damaged

	below 1 psi below 35 mph many broken windows	1 psi (approx) 35 mph (approx) most windows broken

facing the shock wave might not because of the increase in pressure caused by reflection, and most if not the whole of the building could collapse. Thirdly, the blast wave from the explosion of large nuclear bombs can take several seconds to pass completely, so the maximum overpressure and wind speed may persist for this period. If there were enough doors and windows open (or blasted out), the extra pressure would force air into the building and as soon as the wave had passed, it would explode. About 10 miles (16 km) from a 10-Mt explosion, for example, the blast overpressure

Atomic destruction and pollution in the Nevada Desert, 1953.

would take about eight seconds to pass. At this range the overpressure could reach about 4 psi above atmospheric pressure. This is quite enough to flatten most buildings, but the tremendous pressure built up in the eight seconds of the blast wave's passage would cause most buildings which remained standing to explode.

Blast effects on people

Blast pressures capable of destroying a house could leave humans physically unharmed. The body is flexible and small. It bends on impact, and when squashed the internal pressure quickly rises to equal the external pressure.

An overpressure of 5 psi could possibly rupture eardrums, though not if the ears were protected. Ten psi overpressure (enough to bring down even earthquake-resistant reinforced concrete buildings) might cause slight bleeding in the lungs.

Up to 30 psi pressure could cause severe lung haemorrhage and 40 psi could kill. (But anybody close enough to an explosion to experience 40 psi overpressure would almost certainly be killed by other bomb effects.)

The main danger to people in the open air at the time of an explosion would be being struck by flying glass and debris, or being thrown bodily by the wind pressure against hard objects. Five miles (8 km) from a 1-Mt air burst, for example, the blast overpressure of up to 4 psi would destroy houses but leave people uninjured. But many would be killed or smashed by being dragged along in winds of up to 130 mph (210 km/h) and hurled into solid objects, or they would be severely lacerated by flying glass.

Calculating the amount of blast destruction

The testing of nuclear weapons has made it possible to make detailed predictions about the amount of damage done at different ranges from explosions of various weapon powers. An invaluable reference for precise details is the US Government's publication *The Effects of Nuclear Weapons*, in which full documentation of the types of damage and possible mechanisms are given. Inserted into the back cover of the book is a Nuclear Bomb Effects Computer: a circular slide rule which enables you to make quick accurate calculations of all of the main effects. It is *very important* to note, however, that many factors could change these effects: a bomb might not explode properly, so that only a fraction of its energy was released; hills could reflect blast and heat and channel winds, and many aspects of the weather – rainfall, visibility, temperature of different air layers and winds – could all change the effects of nuclear weapons. So it is only possible to give *approximate* figures for the amount of damage which might occur in *average* places under *average* conditions.

The amount of blast damage depends almost exclusively on the blast overpressure produced by the explosion. This is highest at or below the explosion ('ground

Effects of a weapon air-burst (unless otherwise stated) at optimum height*

weapon yield	1-kt	150-kt	1-Mt	10-Mt	20-Mt
fireball max. size	220 ft	1,580 ft	3,400 ft	8,450 ft	11,350 ft
min. height of explosion for no local fallout	180 ft	1,320 ft	2,750 ft	6,850 ft	9,250 ft
crater width (inner lip)†	126 ft	530 ft	950 ft	1,800 ft	2,300 ft
crater depth†	28 ft	140 ft	210 ft	420 ft	530 ft
range of lethal initial radiation (500 r)	0.5 miles	1.2 miles	1.6 miles	2.5 miles	3 miles
range for skin reddening	0.5 miles	5.5 miles	10 miles	24 miles	30 miles
range for charred skin	0.4 miles	3.5 miles	8 miles	18 miles	23 miles
range for 2% buildings gutted by fire (2 psi blast)	0.8 miles	4.2 miles	8 miles	17 miles	22 miles
range for 10% buildings gutted by fire (5 psi blast)	0.4 miles	2.2 miles	4.3 miles	9.3 miles	12 miles
range for fatal wind drag (a human could be dragged along at 40 ft/sec)	0.2 miles	1.6 miles	3.3 miles	8 miles	10 miles
duration of severe blast (4 psi)	0.3 secs	1.8 secs	3 secs	7 secs	9 secs
arrival time of blast wave (4 psi)	2 secs after flash	10 secs after flash	20 secs after flash	42 secs after flash	53 secs after flash
range of devastation for above-ground buildings (12 psi)	0.3 miles	1.3 miles	2.5 miles	5 miles	7 miles
range of severe blast damage (4 psi)	0.5 miles	2.6 miles	5 miles	11 miles	13 miles
range at which all windows broken (1 psi)	1.3 miles	7 miles	13 miles	28 miles	36 miles

*The range of effects required dictates the explosion's optimum height, eg when a 1-Mt weapon is exploded at 5,000 ft there is a 1.2 mile range of devastation, compared to a 4.4 mile range when the height of explosion is 10,000 ft.

†surface-burst only

Source: Calculated from the 'Nuclear Bomb Effects Computer' included in Glasstone, Samuel and Dolan, Philip J., The Effects of Nuclear Weapons, 3rd ed.

zero'). The table on pages 28–9 lists the amount of damage done by various blast overpressures.

The fire threat
The risk of the outbreak of severe fires after a nuclear explosion can hardly be overstated. Cities could burn very easily following a large scale nuclear attack, as would forests and other vegetation including farm crops. Fire could not only devastate urban civilisation, it could also threaten the life of farm livestock and the natural habitat of many wild animals and plants. A 'fire zone' could extend 5 miles (8 km) in all directions from the explosive

point of a 1-Mt bomb. It would be possible to convert every city in Europe, the United States and the Soviet Union into a fire zone using only a small fraction of the present day nuclear arsenal. Work out the risk for yourself: draw circles of 5-mile (8-km) radius over towns and cities on a map. Not many such circles are needed to account for the greater part of civilised habitation in the world.

Fire storms

Hiroshima was engulfed in a fire storm following the explosion of the atom bomb above it in 1945. So many fires were started by the heat flash that they all joined together in the central area and raged away like an enormous blow-torch, sucking air from outside until everything combustible was burnt. Firestorms also happened in some German cities bombed during the Second World War. Once a fire storm had begun, nothing could stop it until everything was burnt. It would not only destroy buildings and property, but also burn up oxygen from the air, so that even people in deep, heat-resistant shelters could die of suffocation.

Nobody knows for certain how easily nuclear explosions would cause fire storms: Nagasaki did not suffer from one although there was widespread burning.

Conflagration

Whether or not fire storms did occur, however, fires could start which spread out of control. Called conflagrations, these could extend to and devastate regions far removed from the areas of the other weapon effects. This is what happened in Nagasaki: the distribution of buildings and the hilly terrain prevented a fire storm but favoured a conflagration. Especially with the radiation hazards of nuclear weapons it would be unlikely that any effective fire-fighting could be carried out. Huge numbers of people could be burnt to death and many others could die from the effects of less severe burns.

Burns

Because so much of the nuclear bomb's energy is generated in the form of heat the most common injuries among survivors would probably be burns. Victims 23 miles away from a 20-Mt explosion standing in the open could suffer from charred skin (third degree burns) on parts of the body not covered by clothes. The same effect could be produced 8 miles away from a 1-Mt explosion and at this range many fires would be started by the heat flash.

The medical problem of treating hundreds of thousands of burns victims on the fringes of each explosion would be insuperable. Most would die painfully because of lack of medical facilities.

Sources of uncertainty

All effects of nuclear weapons are uncertain by large factors, so it is by no means definite that because a weapon of a particular yield is targeted to a particular point a known sequence of events will take place. In fact the actual events may be completely different from those suggested by the theory. One reason is that the bomb may not reach its target: it may miss by hundreds of feet or several miles. The effects of a near miss could be totally different from a direct hit if, for example, a hill stood between the intended target and the actual point of impact. Secondly the bomb might not explode efficiently: the fission and fusion reactions might not proceed fully, so a 10-Mt bomb might only produce an explosion equivalent to a much smaller device or no explosion at all. Most uncertain of all is the weather: heavy rainfall would almost completely eliminate the hazard of serious fires even though some could start. Fog or low cloud could prevent light and heat radiating out from the fireball, and strong winds could produce at least two effects: they could help push the warhead off-course, and they would blow fallout and debris. You could be just a few miles upwind of ground zero in a strong gale and torrential rain with low clouds and be saved by the weather from heat, some of the blast, light-flash and fallout. Yet another uncertainty is terrain: hills and tall buildings reflect blast and cast shadows shielding other places from light and heat in a way which could greatly change the bomb effects.

An attack on Kennedy Airport, New York

The rings on the maps mark the maximum ranges of the effects produced by nuclear weapons air burst above New York City. **Right** For a 150-kt bomb: (A) lethal initial radiation; 12 psi overpressure – complete devastation of all normal buildings; (B) severe risk of fire storm or conflagration; (C) 4 psi overpressure – most ordinary houses destroyed; (D) charring of exposed skin, and (E) 1 psi overpressure – severe damage to windows, doors, roof-tiles: most houses still standing. **Below** For a 20-Mt weapon: (A) lethal initial radiation; (B) 12 psi overpressure; (C) severe fire risk; (D) 4 psi overpressure; (E) skin charred, (F) 1 psi overpressure.

1 inch = approx 14.6 miles
2.5 cm = approx 25 km

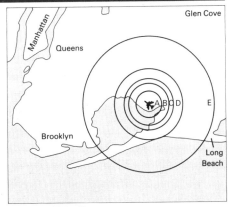

1 inch = approx 10.2 miles
2.5 cm = approx 16 km

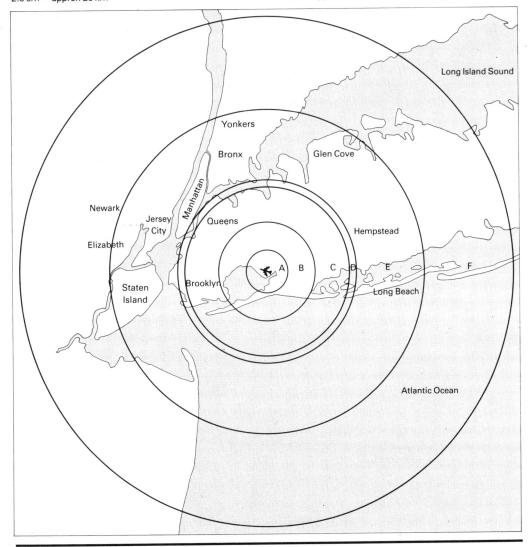

Civilian airports such as Kennedy International Airport in New York City could be targeted in a nuclear attack against the United States. It would be difficult to put such an airfield permanently out of action by totally destroying runways, as this would require the ground detonation of enough warheads to cover the entire area with craters. Use of the airport could be halted for days or weeks, however, by detonating a single weapon in the air. If accurately targeted this could cause enough devastation in the surroundings to block all access roads while at the same time destroying facilities at the airport itself. It would also have the humane advantage of eliminating the risk of local fallout.

The choice of weapon yield for a single-bomb attack on Kennedy Airport would depend on whether more widespread destruction were considered desirable as collateral damage for military or political purposes. A 150-kt bomb

would probably achieve all of the effects necessary to prevent use of the airport temporarily. At 12 times the blast power of the Hiroshima bomb any survivor might describe the utter desolation which would overtake the the airport and its hinterland.

A 1-Mt device would cause far more damage than necessary for destroying the airport. Over a million New Yorkers would die instantly, with a similar number dying days or weeks after the attack. Almost every window in the entire metropolitan area would be shattered by the blast, with extreme devastation, fire and suffering in Queens and Brooklyn.

A 20-Mt bomb could inject such heat into the city that even rain and fog might be dispersed in an instant and fires ignited almost everywhere. This would affect every city inhabitant: if a 20-Mt weapon were chosen, the aim would not be purely the destruction of Kennedy Airport but the annihilation of New York City.

1 inch = approx 9 miles
2.5 cm = approx 14.5 cm

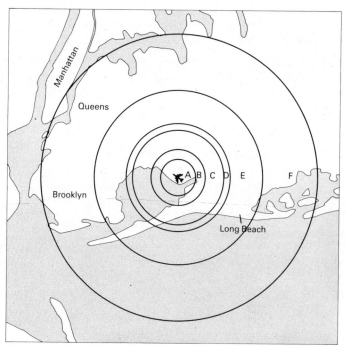

A 1-Mt weapon used against Kennedy Airport in New York City (**left and right**) would probably be air burst at about 10,000 feet (3,000 m) to maximise the area receiving at least 4 psi overpressure (D), sufficient to destroy most houses and ordinary buildings. The burnt and irradiated victims below the explosive point would experience only ten seconds of agony before the blast wave struck. Further towards Manhattan, at (E), people would see the flash and perhaps receive severe burns at the moment of detonation. But they would not feel the 70 mph (110 km/h) winds and the blast wave until 40 seconds later. Sweeping relentlessly on, the blast wave would break nearly every window on Manhattan where streets would be littered with glass.

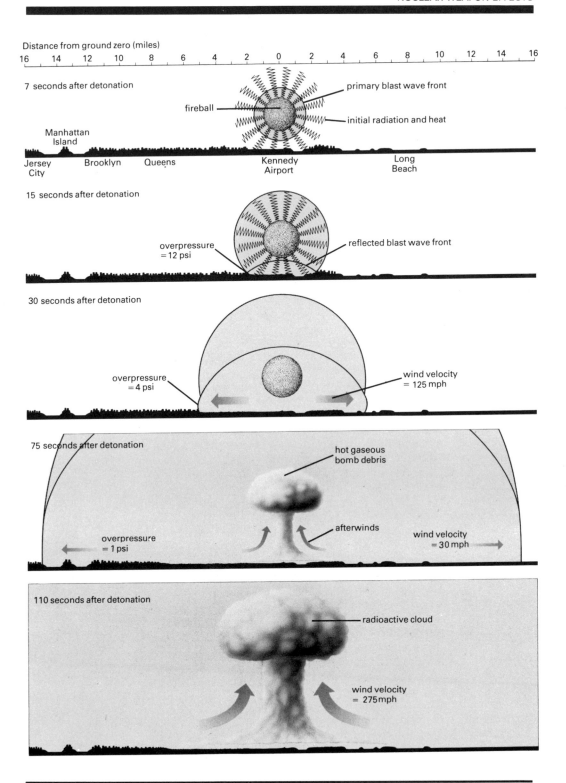

Distance from ground zero (miles)

16 14 12 10 8 6 4 2 0 2 4 6 8 10 12 14 16

7 seconds after detonation

fireball

primary blast wave front

initial radiation and heat

Manhattan
Island

Jersey
City

Brooklyn   Queens

Kennedy
Airport

Long
Beach

15 seconds after detonation

overpressure
= 12 psi

reflected blast wave front

30 seconds after detonation

overpressure
= 4 psi

wind velocity
= 125 mph

75 seconds after detonation

hot gaseous
bomb debris

afterwinds

overpressure
= 1 psi

wind velocity
= 30 mph

110 seconds after detonation

radioactive cloud

wind velocity
= 275 mph

Radiation

Initial radiation

Radiation is one of the most fearful aspects of nuclear warfare. Invisible, it is also undetectable by the other human senses, and yet it is lethal. The explosive energy of nuclear fission and fusion processes produce huge numbers of fast neutrons. At the same time the immense release of energy generates x-rays and gamma rays: both are electromagnetic waves, similar in basic nature to light waves and radio waves, but far more energetic (having very short wavelengths) and therefore penetrating and dangerous to humans. The flash of radiation produced at the time of explosion is called initial radiation. The fallout radiation, which continues to be a hazard after the explosion, is called 'delayed radiation'.

Initial radiation is harmful within only a limited range because as the gamma rays and neutrons travel outwards from the explosion they become weakened by spreading out and becoming absorbed in the atmosphere. The x-rays are absorbed even before leaving the fireball.

But the larger weapons (a few hundred kilotons upwards in power) would produce so much blast and heat that anybody close enough to receive lethal amounts of initial radiation would almost certainly not survive death by blast injury or burning. If people were exposed to low-yield weapons, however, they might be killed by initial radiation. The 12.5-kt Hiroshima bomb inflicted initial radiation damage on many people. Modern weapons of 1 kt designed for use on the battlefield could kill victims far beyond the range of heat and blast effects by exposure to neutron and gamma radiations.

Delayed radiation: fallout

The feature which makes nuclear bombs uniquely powerful, the fission and fusion of nuclei, also creates the hazard of fallout radiation which is not encountered with ordinary explosives. When fission takes place uranium and plutonium nuclei do not all split into the same types of fragments. More than 300 different isotopes – the fission products – may be formed. Some of these – those which exist normally in nature and whose nuclei are identical with those of atoms found widely in ordinary materials – may be stable. But many of the fission products are very unstable. Their nuclei can erupt like volcanoes, spewing forth electrons and gamma rays with great vehemence. These are 'radioisotopes' which can fall to earth as fallout. Not every unstable nucleus erupts at the same moment. If this happened all the radiation would emerge in an instant and there would be no remaining fallout hazard. Each nucleus has a statistical chance of decaying by ejecting radiation within a period of time (which differs for each isotope). But at the end of that time some will have decayed whereas others will continue holding on to their pent-up energies.

Half-life

The 'half-life' of any particular radioisotope is the length of time taken for half of the atomic nuclei in a particular sample of the isotope to erupt and transform themselves into the nuclei of other atoms by emitting radiation. After two half-lives, only one-quarter of the atoms will be left, after three half-lives one-eighth and so on.

Half-lives of radioisotopes

aluminium–28	2.3 minutes
barium–140	12.8 days
carbon–14	5,730 years
cesium–137	30 years
chlorine–38	37 minutes
iodine–131	8 days
manganese–56	2.6 hours
oxygen–16	7 seconds
plutonium–239	24,000 years
silicon–31	2.6 hours
sodium–24	15 hours
strontium–90	27.7 years
tritium	12.3 years

Source: Glasstone, Samuel and Dolan, Philip J., *The Effects of Nuclear Weapons*, 3rd ed.

Before the signing of the Partial Test Ban Treaty bombs were exploded in as many different environments as possible. The underwater burst at Bikini Atoll in July 1946 (right) created a spectacular hollow waterspout (below) containing a million tons of water reaching 6,000 feet (2,000 m) into the air. The battleship *Arkansas* (sunk by the explosion) may have been lifted by the waterspout and then dropped back into the sea. Intense fallout was created because radioactive fission products, bomb residues and water fell into the sea having risen only to 10,000 feet (3,300 m).

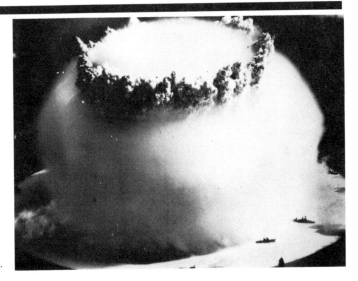

Range of half-lives

Some fission products have half-lives of just a few minutes so all of their atoms disappear soon after the explosion. But the full range of the many different radioisotopes produced by a nuclear explosion includes those which have half-lives of thousands of years (see table on page 36).

The shortest-lived isotopes are the most hazardous soon after the explosion, because most of their atoms erupt and produce radiation. The long-lived isotopes produce smaller amounts of radiation in a given length of time but continue to do so for many years. They can create a serious long-term risk to health and life by entering the environment and the food chain and getting trapped within the body.

Reduction of the hazard with time

All atoms of radioisotopes in fallout have a statistical likelihood of decaying and becoming stable substances not hazardous to life as the amount of radiation emitted by fallout decreases as time goes by. Many of the isotopes have very short half-lives and tests have shown that seven hours after an explosion the amount of radiation is only one-tenth as much as one hour after detonation. This is sometimes called the seven-tenths rule. Extending this to a period of 49 hours (7 × 7 hours) the rate of radiation dosage is reduced to one-hundredth of its initial value. After two weeks (7 × 7 × 7 hours) it has fallen to one-thousandth. This factor of 1,000 is sufficient to reduce the radiation dose rate to relatively safe levels. This is why two weeks is often quoted as 'the shelter period'.

Warning: Although the seven-tenths rule demonstrates dramatically how quickly radioactivity can fall off as time passes, there is no substitute for actually measuring the strength of radiation with instruments such as radiation dose-meters and Geiger Counters (see page 91). Fallout can be far more concentrated in some places (such as where heavy rain has fallen) than others and even though the radiation decreases with time it could begin at a very high level in such a 'hot spot'. A further reason for caution is that the seven-tenths rule should not be taken too literally: it was

worked out from tests and calculations taking note of the quantities and half-lives of all isotopes likely to be present in most nuclear explosions, but nobody can be sure whether an explosion would proceed as the textbook says it should. Special weapons could even be used with extra elements designed to *increase* fallout contamination with selected isotopes.

How fallout is made and descends to earth

In air-burst explosions the fallout consists of very fine dust which is a mixture of fission products, bomb construction materials, atoms of air and other substances in the atmosphere such as water vapour and pollutants. Surface bursts draw huge quantities of earth and other material into the fireball. This vaporizes, collects fission products, then cools, forming larger fallout particles, some as big as snowflakes and marbles, which fall to earth much more quickly than the fine dust of an air burst. In addition to this, the original surface materials become radioactive themselves (by absorbing fast neutrons) and add to the concentration of radiation produced by the fission products.

Thus fallout would be a far more severe local problem if a surface burst took place.

Global fallout

All nuclear explosions in the earth's atmosphere cause distant fallout, however, be-

The fireball (1) forms a cloud (from a low-yield weapon (2); high-yield weapon (3)). Radioactive particles drift in the atmosphere (4), mix with rain clouds (5) and fall (6) to contaminate the ground (7).

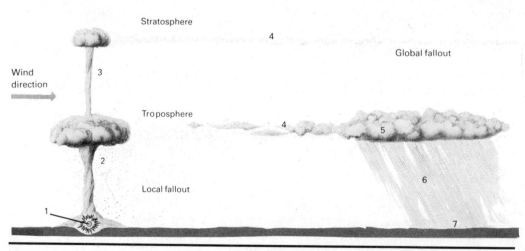

Stratosphere

4

Global fallout

Wind direction

3

Troposphere

4

5

2

6

Local fallout

1

7

The radioactive fallout plume created by a nuclear explosion would bend whenever the wind changed direction. In this example of a 1-Mt surface burst on Tel Aviv we assume that the wind speed is constant at 15 mph (24 km/h), but that it changes direction twice: veering from north-westerly (at the time of the explosion) to south-westerly two hours later, and after a further three hours to southerly.

The contours indicate the dose accumulated by anyone out in the open for a period of seven days immediately following the explosion. (If the wind were constant the plume would form a cigar-shaped pattern.)

In Jerusalem, over 30 miles (48 km) from Tel Aviv, the accumulated radiation dose would be 3,000 r in one week; a further 40 miles (64 km) downwind in Amman, people could suffer the still lethal dose of 900 r, and at Damascus (about 100 miles (160 km) from Amman) the dose would be 300 r.

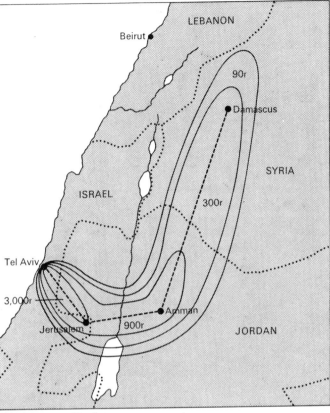

1 inch = approx 50 miles
2.5 cm = approx 78.5 km

cause some of the fission products inevitably take the form of very fine dust which can stay at high altitude for long periods of time. For weapons with explosive yields from 100 kt upwards such particles rise into the stratosphere more than 30,000 feet (10 km) and can remain there for many years because this is above the altitude up to which particles can be 'scoured' by rainfall (most rain clouds are below this altitude). This stratospheric pollution with radioisotopes causes a global fallout hazard, with longer-lived isotopes, such as stron-tium 90 (half-life: 28 years), gradually falling to earth in widely dispersed places over many years. Global fallout would affect all countries, including ones which might not have been attacked with nuclear weapons. If enough of the bombs *already in existence* were ever to be exploded it is possible that the global fallout would reach dangerous levels for everybody on earth, and the prospect of a polluted world in which everybody surviving is exposed to hazardous levels of radiation after a nuclear war is entirely possible.

3 How radiation affects people

The danger from radiation cannot be stressed too much. You cannot see, hear, smell, taste or feel radiation and yet it can deliver a lethal blow in seconds. It is not even a kind killer. Death from radiation is almost always excruciatingly painful and protracted.

When radiation fails to kill, it can leave its mark on your body: sterility, leukaemia, cancer, inherited disorders, birth defects and many other conditions may result from the destructive effect radiation has on living cells.

Because radiation is such an effective killer, it is even possible that in a nuclear war it could be used as the primary weapon. The neutron bomb is specifically designed to kill people by neutron radiation. Other nuclear weapons can be specially 'salted' with elements which can inflict additional radiation damage. Even defensive anti-missile systems can consist of guided nuclear bombs which explode near an incoming missile – releasing fallout close to the defending country. There would be, indeed, no escape from the radiation problem if nuclear war began.

Harmful radiations

Not all radiation is harmful. Heat and light are forms which normally do no damage at all. The unique, distinguishing feature which makes nuclear radiation so dangerous is that it causes 'ionisation', or static electricity, among the atoms of any material it passes through. This happens when electrons are torn away from their positions surrounding atoms. Atoms consist of a nucleus charged with positive electricity surrounded by electrons charged with negative electricity (see page 15). When the ionising radiations separate these charges by removing electrons, atoms and free electrons react swiftly with other atoms or collections of atoms (molecules). In so doing they can greatly damage living tissue.

Our bodies are built up from billions of cells. Although each cell is no bigger than a hundredth part of a millimetre it contains a complex structure of atoms. Cells have the remarkable property of being able to reproduce themselves, and each human cell contains a set of instructions, a blueprint which specifies the structure of the cell. All of our bodily characteristics, hair colour, height, skin colour and so on, are coded like a computer programme in the genetic blueprint contained within each and every cell of the body. In theory it is possible to grow an entire human being (a clone) from a single human cell.

The entire, beautiful form of a living cell is held together by electrical forces. The tiny attractions between atomic nuclei (which are positively charged) and electrons (negatively charged) cement the different parts of the cell together. Although atoms and electrons within the cell move about to some extent, this motion is so tiny that the basic formation is very rarely disturbed. Imagine, therefore, what happens when a high-speed nuclear particle or energetic gamma ray enters the cell. The effect is devastating because the energies of ionising radiations far surpass the energies binding the cell parts together.

A human cell

Exposure to radiation

Energy is taken up in
the irradiated material

Ionizations etc

Alterations to cell metabolism

Permanent
modifications in
functioning of
some cells
(caused by
chemical changes)

Microscopically
observable damage
in living tissue

Death of
individual cells
(*eg* gut cells)

Long delayed
effects of radiation
such as genetic
changes or the
induction of cancer

Radiation sickness
(which can lead to
death) in multicellular
organisms

Above When exposed to a similar dose of
radiation, some human cells die whereas others
continue to live and may either remain completely
healthy or develop defects which could lead to
cancer or genetic changes. As the exposure
increases, however, the proportion of cells
unaffected diminishes.

Cells can be so badly damaged that the
elegant order is completely destroyed and
the cell dies. If less radiation damage is
incurred the cell may stay alive but have its
chemistry so totally altered by the impact
that it loses its original pattern. It may thus
live on to become a cancer cell, endlessly
reproducing itself in a grossly abnormal
form. Very slight radiation damage may
possibly be repaired, and in such circumstances normal cell life resumes.

It is unfortunately true, however, that for
reasons which are not understood even tiny
amounts of radiation damage to cells can
sometimes produce serious ill health. So no
amount of ionising radiation, however tiny,
can be dismissed as harmless.

Types of radiation

Some forms of ionising radiation are beams
of pure energy, rather like light but capable
of penetrating materials. Others consist of
particles: minute, invisible pieces of matter,
some carrying electrical charges, others not.
The most important types of ionising radiation are described below:

X-rays consist of waves, like light waves but
much shorter, carrying more energy. They
are used in medicine because of their ability
to penetrate the body, particularly the
fleshy parts, and reveal internal ab-
normalities on x-ray photographs. Even

Below Because alpha and beta radiations consist of
particles which collide with atoms in other
materials, they can hardly penetrate solid materials
at all, unlike gamma rays which are waves of light
and are very energetic.

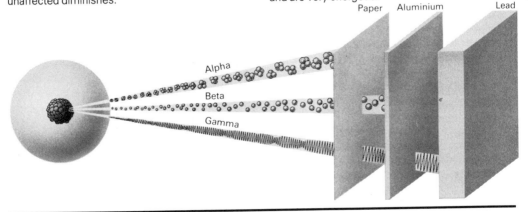

Paper　Aluminium　Lead

Alpha

Beta

Gamma

medical x-rays are dangerous to a slight extent.

Gamma rays are similar to x-rays but have a shorter wave length and are more energetic and more damaging. The fireball of a nuclear explosion produces an intense pulse of gamma rays. Fallout dust emits gamma radiation continuously and this is the most severe risk after a nuclear attack.

Beta particles are electrons which have been freed from the nuclei of atoms. They can only penetrate a few millimetres of human flesh. The main risk from beta radiation occurs if fallout producing it is accidentally swallowed or inhaled. In this way a radiation dose can be delivered continuously to sensitive internal organs rather than to skin, which is not very sensitive to radiation.

Alpha particles are the nuclei of helium atoms, stripped bare of electrons. They are heavy, carry an electric charge, and penetrate less than 1 millimetre through body tissues. Alpha particles outside the body are of little importance. But if fallout which contains isotopes releasing alpha particles is swallowed or inhaled, the radiation dose to internal organs can be dangerous.

Neutrons: One of the basic particles out of which atomic nuclei are made, a neutron carries no electricity and this helps it penetrate deeply within body tissues because it is unaffected by the positive and negative charges in the matter through which it passes. If it is absorbed by the nucleus of another atom, however, it can make that atom unstable and radioactive, forming an additional radiation hazard. Fallout produces few neutrons. The initial fireball of a nuclear explosion produces many. The neutron bomb is designed to produce as much neutron radiation as possible.

Exposure to these harmful radiations from the fireball and from fallout can cause radiation sickness and long-term effects.

Units for measuring radiation

The Roentgen
The roentgen (abbreviated to r) describes the amount of ionisation produced when radiation is absorbed in air. Radiation has a strength of one roentgen if it causes a specified amount of ionisation in one cubic inch of dry air at a standard temperature and pressure. The amount of ionisation is proportional to the energy content of the radiation, so the roentgen is a measure of energy.

The Rad
For measuring radiation effects, however, it is more important to know how much energy is absorbed in a material when a particular amount of radiation shines through it. So a unit called the rad (radiation absorbed dose) is used. The same strength of radiation (measured in roentgens) can result in different amounts of absorbed energy in different materials, because some substances absorb radiation more easily than others. Human flesh, however, absorbs almost exactly one rad when one roentgen of radiation shines on one cubic inch of it. So,

when talking about radiation doses to humans, one rad is almost the same as one roentgen. Descriptions of doses are usually given in roentgens.

The Rem
Some forms of ionising radiation do more damage to human cells than others, even when the dose of radiation damage, the rem (roentgen equivalent man) has been defined as the amount of radiation required to cause a particular amount of biological damage. High speed neutrons and alpha particles, for example, do ten times as much damage as the same dose (in roentgens) of x-rays or gamma rays. This means that one roentgen of alpha particles produces ten rems of biological damage in humans, whereas one r of gamma rays produces only one rem of damage.

So although it may be confusing to see radiation doses given in three different units: r, rad, or rem, these units would be almost exactly the same as each other for the purpose of making most calculations of radiation dosage during and after an attack.

Radiation sickness

The symptoms of radiation sickness usually occur when a person has received at least 150 r of whole-body radiation over a short period of time, *ie* up to a few days.

Immediate symptoms

A person receiving a dose of 450 r has, on average only a 50 per cent chance of surviving. This is called the 'LD 50 dose', and the symptoms of radiation sickness described below are those which result from radiation doses at about this level. A dose of about 600 r will kill almost anybody exposed to it but, as with almost any case of radiation sickness, death may be delayed for days or weeks.

Within a few hours of exposure to doses at about the LD 50 level, a person might feel nausea, vomit (possibly repeatedly) and develop diarrhoea. These symptoms could begin within half an hour of exposure, or could be delayed for several hours. If they disappeared after one or two days, the person might survive. If the symptoms continued with vomiting and diarrhoea increasing, the person could develop exhaustion, fever, perhaps delirium and might die a week or so after exposure.

Victims who recovered from the early symptoms of sickness and diarrhoea might feel fairly well, though tired, and have little appetite, but tests would show a fall in the number of white cells in the blood. After two weeks, new symptoms could arise: hair might start to fall out; then, from about the third week onwards, small haemorrhages might be noticed in the skin and the mucous membranes of the mouth. These areas could have a tendency to bruise easily and there might be bleeding from the gums. Ulcerations could develop in the mouth and throat and in the bowels, causing diarrhoea again. Complete loss of appetite, loss of weight and high fever might follow. People as ill as this would not be able to eat and healing wounds would break down and become infected.

At this stage the number of red cells in the blood would be below normal and this condition of anaemia would increase until the fourth or fifth week after exposure. The fall in the number of white cells (first noted two days after exposure) would have progressed, impairing the body's ability to fight infection. Evidence from Nagasaki and Hiroshima shows that infections of all kinds were rife among victims of the bomb.[1] Many of those affected would die at this stage, a month or so after exposure. Those who survived would recover very slowly and, even after recovery, they might die suddenly from an infection which would cause a minor illness in a healthy person.

How radiation causes these symptoms

As we have seen, the principal effect of ionising radiation is to inject sudden, excessive energy into living cells and thus to damage them. Cells have the ability to reproduce themselves, but some do this more quickly than others. Rapidly dividing tissues are very much more sensitive to radiation than tissues where the cells are reproducing more slowly. The human gut is an area of rapidly dividing tissue and radiation damage there would lead directly to the symptoms of nausea, vomiting and diarrhoea. Damage to the gut could also allow bowel contents to enter the bloodstream and cause infection. Haemorrhages might appear at the site of gut damage as well as in other radiation-damaged tissues, leading to loss of blood and anaemia.

Bone marrow cells are also rapidly dividing and sensitive to radiation. They manufacture most of the white blood cells with which a healthy person combats infections. Destruction of the bone marrow thus would make the victim vulnerable to a wide range of infections against which he or she no longer had adequate natural defences.

Some of the white cells in the bone marrow are also responsible for manufacturing the blood cells called platelets. In a healthy person these help the blood to form clots which stop severe haemorrhage at wounds or other sites of damage. Killing bone marrow cells removes the platelets' source and the victim could more easily bleed to death.

Effects resulting from rapid whole-body doses of ionising radiation

Dose	Vomiting incidence	Initial phase†	Latent phase†† duration	Final phase††† duration	Main organ involved
0–100 r No illness					
100–200r Slight illness	100r: seldom 200r: common	Begins after 3–6 hours. Continues up to 1 day	up to 2 weeks	up to 2 weeks	blood forming systems: bone marrow, lymph glands
200–600r* Survival possible	above 300r: all	Begins after ½–6 hours. Continues up to 1–2 days	1–4 weeks	1–8 weeks	blood forming systems: bone marrow, lymph glands
600–1000r Survival possible	all	Begins after ¼–½ hour. Continues up to 2 days	5–10 days	1–4 weeks	blood forming systems: bone marrow, lymph glands
1000–5000r Lethal range	all	Begins after 5–30 minutes. Continues up to 1 day	0–7 days	2–10 days	gastro-intestinal tract
over 5000r	all	almost immediately	no latent phase	1–48 hours Final	central nervous system

*The LD 50 is 450r.
Source: Glasstone, Samuel and Dolan, Philip J., *The Effects of Nuclear Weapons*, 3rd ed.

†initial phase
(nausea; vomiting; headache; dizziness; loss of appetite; tiredness – severity increases with dose)

††latent phase
(apparent recovery but changes continuing in blood-forming tissues; gut and nerve tissue complications develop at higher doses)

†††final phase
(high temperature and fever with all symptoms of initial phase; bleeding and bruising affecting skin, mouth, lips and gut; blood in urine; lower resistance to infection could lead to ulceration; diarrhoea; loss of hair; delirium (as temperature rises out of control); emaciation (through not eating); seizures; extreme pain)

Some of the body's white cells for fighting infection, the lymphocytes, are manufactured in the lymph nodes and spleen. These organs also make the natural chemicals called antibodies, another of the body's weapons against disease. Radiation damage to the lymphatic system could thus impair still further the body's defences against disease.

How to treat radiation sickness
Radiation can destroy vital organs so there

Distinguishing signs	Critical period	Treatment	Convalescence period	Incidence of death	Death occurs within
above 50r; slight changes in blood cells					
moderate fall in white blood cell count		reassurance; antibiotics if infections start	several weeks		
Severe loss of white blood cells; bleeding; infection; anaemia (loss of red blood cells); loss of hair (above 300r)	1–6 weeks	as before, and blood transfusion; give fluids and salt for shock	1–12 months	0–90%	2–12 weeks
	1–6 weeks	as before, and bone marrow transplant if possible; antibiotics essential	long	90–100%	2–12 weeks
diarrhoea; fever; shock symptoms	2–14 days	fluids and salt to alleviate shock symptoms: no hope of recovery so no transfusions or transplant		100%	2–14 days
convulsions; tremor; involuntary movements; lethargy	1–48 hours	terminal care: sedatives, pain killers		100%	up to days

can be no wonder cure for radiation sickness. Some drugs given *before* radiation exposure could limit the damage to a slight extent, but care after exposure would normally be limited to easing the symptoms and supporting the patient by good nursing. In many cases this could make all the difference between life and death. If, for example, only one per cent of the bone marrow's cells remained undamaged after exposure these could reproduce and eventually replace the cells which had died. If the patient were nursed carefully he or she might thus survive.

Without hospital facilities the best help you could give victims of radiation sickness would be to keep them warm and comfortable in bed. You could give pain killing drugs if you had them, taking care not to overload the patient with drugs which the disturbed metabolism might not be able to tolerate. Vitamins and mineral tablets could help replace vital nutrients which had been lost because of vomiting and other symptoms. If you had access to them, antibiotics could be used when infections developed.

Patients might find it impossible to eat, but it would be important to try giving them as much water as they could comfortably drink to combat the dehydrating effect of the stomach and gut symptoms.

If you were lucky enough to get the patient to a working hospital he or she could be fed intravenously, and there is a possibility that bone marrow transplantation could be of some help, though this is not by any means an easy or trouble-free treatment. Blood transfusions could be given to replace lost blood and thus combat anaemia. Drugs which control shock symptoms and medicines to reduce bleeding could also be used. Whether any of the treatments mentioned could actually save many lives is open to question. Death might be delayed, but if the underlying damage were severe enough the patient would still die.

Long-term effects

Those who survived the initial onslaught of radiation sickness resulting from short-term doses greater than 150r or thereabouts would nevertheless face the risk of a wide range of possible long-term complications. People who had been exposed to less than about 150r of radiation would also face the same long-term hazards, though to a lesser degree (so far as is known). And radiation doses as low as 1r per week are thought to contribute to ill health many years later.

Evidence from Hiroshima and Nagasaki[2] shows that radiation victims (who had received large, but not lethal doses) were four times more likely to suffer from leukaemia than other people. Even so the risk is still quite small: on average, about one person in 100 who are heavily exposed will develop the disease. When they do, the disease begins a few years after exposure.

Nearly all of the early pioneers of radioactivity (the scientists who discovered x-rays and first learned to use them in medical diagnosis) developed cancer later in life.[3] Generally this was 20 or 30 years after their exposure to radiation. The early uranium miners (at the end of the last century) often developed 'mountain sickness', later shown to be lung cancer, as a result of inhaling radon, the radioactive gas which comes from uranium ores.[4] Cancer commonly affected factory workers who painted radium onto watch and clock faces to make them luminous (particularly those who licked their brushes while working).[5] Medical treatments and diagnosis using x-rays have also been known to cause cancer in many people.[6] All of these activities are now carefully controlled but it is clear that large-scale contamination with radioactive fallout from nuclear warfare would produce major epidemics of cancer 20 or even more years later.

High doses of radiation can cause the lens of the eye to become opaque – a condition called cataract. This would be likely to happen in people who had survived near-lethal doses. Even then, not all vision might be lost.

The early x-ray pioneers handled radioactive materials frequently, receiving large doses of radiation to the hands.[7] This led to reddening of the skin, warts, running sores, extreme pain, gross deformities and often cancer at the site of radiation injury: the full list of these ailments took many years to develop in different victims. Fallout dust which stuck to the skin, clothes and hair could cause skin burns, especially from beta radiations which would then be close enough to have an effect, adding to the dose from gamma rays produced by fallout. It would be extremely important to wash off any fallout and to remove contaminated clothes.

Radiation can reduce the fertility of men and women and if the dose is large enough make them permanently sterile.[8] A dose of about 500r delivered to the ovaries or testes would be likely to produce permanent sterility. Similar doses could produce temporary sterility which lasts for several years. Women are born with their full complement of unfertilised eggs. These eggs are all targets for radiation. In men sperms are manufactured constantly, so although existing sperms might be damaged, future sperms would be spared, provided the organs that manufactured them were undamaged.

An unborn child in its mother's womb is more susceptible to radiation than adults or even children. Radiation exposure during the few weeks immediately after conception (before embryonic limbs and other organs had begun to take shape) could easily cause an abortion. The foetus is at the most vulnerable between the second and sixth weeks following conception. If the foetus suffered radiation exposure then, when the organs were first being formed, a wide range of birth defects could result – such conditions as cleft palate, short limbs, fusion of the ribs and similar deformities, right through to severe disturbance of the central nervous system leading to mentally retarded babies.

Many diseases are thought to be caused by defects in the body's inheritance mechanisms. We inherit characteristics from our parents by means of the complex DNA molecules within each cell of our bodies. The DNA molecule is like a long string with 'beads' on it. Collections of beads form what are called genes, and it is these which tell our body whether to make, for example, blue eyes, black hair and all other bodily characteristics.

If the DNA molecules in human egg or sperm cells were damaged by radiation, however, a completely different gene, a mutation, could be formed. Most mutations produce harmful characteristics such as an increased tendency to contract particular diseases. Although some mutations can be beneficial and lead to stronger, healthier offspring, the harmful mutations are far more common. Because of this there is a great fear that nuclear warfare could lead to vastly increased mutation rates and to a wide range of genetic diseases. Just how severe this risk is has not been established because not enough people have yet been heavily exposed. But the genetic hazards of radiation could turn out to be as important and as devastating as any of the other effects in the very long term.

Background radiation

No amount of ionising radiation, however small, can be said to be harmless. Even a dose of one r per week has been found to depress the number of white cells and just a few roentgens to the foetus can cause birth defects. But even in peacetime we cannot escape exposure to very small amounts of ionising radiation which bombard us continuously throughout our lives. These come from cosmic rays (high-speed nuclear particles coming from the stars and other bodies in space), radioactive elements in the ground and in our food, and from medical x-rays. The growth of nuclear power has led to a very slight increase in this natural background radiation because of minute quantities of radioisotopes released from nuclear power stations. A much more significant increase has been from the fallout injected into the atmosphere by the many experimental explosions of nuclear weapons.

Tolerance to low doses

Although such background radiation may cause damage it is an historical fact that humans are capable of tolerating it. Each person on earth receives no more than a few tenths of a roentgen of background radiation each year. It is only when the dose rises significantly above this figure that we have cause for concern. There is a great deal of argument about the precise level or dosage at which radiation can be said to be harmful, but there is unanimous agreement among doctors that the dose rates resulting from nuclear weapons exploded on inhabited countries would be very harmful indeed.

4 Where will the bombs fall?

No part of the world could expect to be spared from the effects of nuclear weapons if nuclear war began. However some regions would be directly targeted and would suffer from the immediate effects of attack, whereas others might only receive indirect effects of the weapons such as long-term fallout, millions of refugees fleeing from attacked zones, and economic and political chaos. To decide which places are more likely to be attacked directly it is necessary to consider how a war might begin.

Strategic war between the superpowers

A direct exchange of nuclear bombs and missiles between the United States and the Soviet Union remains possible. If it were not possible, or became increasingly implausible, neither country would continue to tolerate the huge level of defence expenditure devoted to strategic arms. The United States' strategic 'triad' of intercontinental ballistic missiles (ICBMs), Strategic Air Command (SAC) long-range nuclear bombers, and missile-carrying submarines forms the three-pronged threat facing the Soviet Union's ICBMs and submarines. How would an attack, using these forces, be mounted?

Submarine-launched missiles are the least accurate of the strategic nuclear delivery systems: although position fixing at sea has improved recently, it is still thought that submarines would be reserved for retaliation. Aircraft carrying air-launched cruise missiles and gravity bombs are highly accurate at reaching targets, but they are slow and vulnerable to detection by enemy radar and so could possibly be shot down by surface-to-air missiles.

While the 'survivability' of aircraft remains a hotly disputed question, targeting accuracy of submarine-launched missiles could be better than is often admitted. But the only strategic weapon delivery system which is accurate, fast, adequately destructive, reliable and against which almost no defensive measure could be taken is the land-based ICBM. So strategic war between the superpowers would, as of the present time, most likely begin with an exchange of ICBMs.

Such an exchange would almost certainly be preceded by intractable political problems elsewhere in the world, such as in the Middle East or Europe: problems with which the superpowers found themselves inextricably linked. So the exchange of ICBMs would almost certainly not come like a bolt from the blue.

A surprise attack

A surprise attack mounted by one superpower against the other, although very unlikely, cannot be totally ruled out. It is just possible that if it were believed that ICBMs could be dispatched efficiently (*ie* with few malfunctions), would work properly in flight and would reach their targets with the desired accuracy, a surprise attack might be mounted by one superpower in an attempt to disarm the other. With present day missile accuracies and reliabilities, however, it is unlikely that one superpower could hope to 'kill' more than 90 per cent of the other's ICBMs, and there would be a risk that the side attacked could launch its ICBMs in retaliation on first sighting of the approaching missiles. (The flight-time for an ICBM travelling between America and the Soviet Union is about 20 minutes, so the response of the attacked side would have to be rapid.)

Such a surprise attack would have to be mounted against ICBM silos, nuclear bombers and submarine bases. In the case of an attack against the United States half of the submarines carrying missiles would be at sea (only 20 per cent of the Soviet submarines are at sea at any one time),[1] and many of the SAC long-range bombers would be airborne (though these might be shot down on their way to Russia). A surprise US attack against the Soviet Union could eliminate 80 per cent of missile-carrying submarines by sinking them at their bases, and by dispatching two warheads on to each Soviet ICBM silo there would be a 90 per cent chance (using unclassified 'lethality' figures available at present[2]) of making a kill (thus reducing retaliation by 90 per cent in the case of the land-based missiles and 80 per cent in the case of the Soviet submarines).

Obviously a surprise attack would bring the penalty that the remaining nuclear forces on either side could still inflict massive retaliatory damage. This is the essence of overkill of course. But as warhead reliability, survivability and targeting accuracy improve each year there could come a time when current overkill capacities are insufficient to deter a surprise attack. More importantly, if politicians *believed* the missiles to be efficient enough (whether or not this turned out to be true in the event) an attack might be mounted in an attempt to limit the damage by retaliation.

While a surprise attack by one superpower against the other is probably the least likely way in which nuclear war might begin, it is possible that during the course of a conventional war elsewhere involving the superpowers, one side would strike first because of a growing certainty that the other was about to do so. Under these conditions the question of limiting damage at home by making the first strike would

assume paramount importance: if convinced you are going to be attacked anyway, what is wrong with striking first, especially if you know that by doing so you can eliminate 90 per cent of your enemy's strategic weapons?

The strategic balance of terror is the 'top rung' of the escalation ladder in nuclear war. But being the top rung does not make it any more stable than nuclear confrontation at any other level: the strategic threats between the United States and the Soviet Union are still equivalent to a game of 'dare': they would be meaningless if they were not made seriously. Make no mistake about it, the Pentagon and the Kremlin mean business when they make nuclear threats and build up nuclear arsenals. Both sides hope the weapons will not be needed, while accepting that their use could be necessary.

Where nuclear wars could start

If strategic war between the superpowers is the top rung of the escalation ladder, what are the intermediate steps which could bring the world to that point (dismissing the small probability of a surprise strategic attack)?

It is quite likely that nuclear war could begin in a region of the world where political troubles exist already. Two basic ingredients are needed to make a 'nuclear war theatre'. The obvious one is that you must have nuclear weapons present in the theatre. Secondly there has to be political disagreement in the region which could possibly be resolved by nuclear warfighting. The second requirement cannot easily be fulfilled in practice, but politically it is quite plausible that national leaders might *perceive* a possibility that advantages could be gained by using (or threatening to use, which ultimately amounts to the same thing) nuclear weapons. In the game of deterrence (which necessarily implies nuclear war risks) *perceptions* of political or military advantage are every bit as important as realities. And with their 'backs against the wall' and with a matter of minutes in which to make a decision (the flight time of a missile) they would be very likely to use their own perceptions and

Theatres of tactical nuclear war

The concept of theatre nuclear war has emerged as one of the ways in which the use of nuclear weapons might become thinkable. However, theatres would be very large and the devastation within a theatre could be complete, with a wide range of global consequences even if all-out war between the superpowers were avoided. In most of the potential theatres escalation to strategic (intercontinental) nuclear war would be an ever-present risk.

Europe

The European theatre includes the whole of Europe, Russia, Scandinavia, Iceland and perhaps North Africa. If war broke out now thousands of short-range tactical nuclear devices such as shells from howitzer guns and short-range ballistic missiles like the Soviet 'Scud' and French 'Pluton' missiles could be used. Battle conditions would be intolerable, and neither side could easily gain ground or 'win' such a tactical war. It would be a conflict of attrition, leaving horrendous devastation, loss of military and civilian lives and intense radioactive pollution.

A European war could also involve the use of aircraft and longer range missiles such as Pershing 2 to deliver nuclear bombs on selected targets deep within enemy territory. In practice both such delivery systems might be destroyed at the outbreak of hostilities. Whatever happened there would be an extreme risk of escalation because the superpowers would be involved from the outset.

China and The Soviet Union

China's growing nuclear arsenal could very soon threaten the whole of the Soviet Union. If the USSR appeared to be 'winning' a war in this huge theatre the USA might be asked to intervene.

Middle East

With Israel's suspected arsenal the concept of deterrence by its nuclear superiority over the Arab countries is already being put to work in the Middle East. Oil interests as well as political alliances could escalate a conflict in this area.

Indo-Pakistan

The whole of India and Pakistan

could become a theatre, which might conceivably be deserted by the superpowers.

Southern Africa
South Africa's suspected possession of nuclear weapons is a cause of concern in a region which has been unstable for a number of years. It is difficult to predict whether the South African Government would use the weapons in internal or external conflicts, or as a menacing deterrent.

beliefs rather than anything else in the decision-making process.

Europe fulfills both requirements for being a candidate nuclear war theatre. There are plenty of nuclear weapons based in Europe and there is a sharp political division between East and West Europe. The European theatre might well stage a nuclear war which could then escalate to strategic exchanges between the superpowers. Alternatively, some 'optimists' hope that only Europe would be devastated and that the superpowers would then negotiate peace and stop short of mutual destruction.

The Middle East is another popular candidate theatre for nuclear war. Israel might have a nuclear arsenal almost ready to go. This is conjecture, however, though almost everybody who has studied the matter seems to agree that this is very likely. Iraq may have a nuclear weapon, and Arab countries may be helping finance the 'first Islamic bomb' which is suspected to be under development in Pakistan. So nuclear weapons could be available to Israel and to their Arab opponents in plausible Middle Eastern nuclear battles. Quite what the superpowers would do about a Middle East nuclear war is uncertain: they might wish to intervene to bring things rapidly to a close. Oil interests would be vitally important, and in the process of superpower involvement such a theatre war could escalate, perhaps by accident. This is conjecture, however, but clearly there are dangers.

India has nuclear weapons and if Pakistan is developing them there is a danger of a nuclear confrontation between the two in the theatre enclosing the region. Again the superpowers might wish to intervene to bring things to a close. Ironically there would be some benefits in not doing so. An Indo-Pakistan theatre nuclear war in the near future would not threaten global devastation because neither country is likely to have enough arms to cause large global effects. Apart from the evidence of Hiroshima and Nagasaki there has been no information about the actual effects of nuclear weapons when used in real warfare. The superpowers have had to rely on theory based on the weapons tests which have been carried out. A limited nuclear war would thus be a 'goldmine' of information about bomb effects. So the superpowers could learn more about nuclear war-fighting by observing such a conflict rather than preventing it. This could either horrify the world so much that a gradual but inexorable move towards world disarmament would begin, or it would refine the methods of deterrence so much that using nuclear weapons became even more believable and thinkable than it is today.

South Africa is thought to have tested a nuclear weapon and might conceivably use it as a strong deterrent against southern African states wishing to threaten its power in that theatre. It is not at all clear, however, how the South African weapons might be used if it came to actual fighting.

A remaining, and very worrying theatre is the Sino-Soviet border: China is rapidly building up an effective arsenal for use against the Soviet Union. The USSR is probably far more worried about a possible Chinese attack at present than one from the relatively friendlier United States. The Chinese take civil defence very seriously, with increasing numbers of protective shelters, and although this might not improve the chances significantly that civilians would survive a Russian attack, such measures are undoubtedly a boost for Chinese morale. The simultaneous build-up of both shelters and the missile arsenal looks very aggressive to the Russians and the Sino-Soviet border is now considered a candidate nuclear war theatre.

War in Europe

A very wide variety of nuclear weapons exist in both East and West Europe and opinions differ widely about the usefulness of each part of the European deterrent. Britain's Ministry of Defence, for example, regards the soon-to-be-adopted ground-launched cruise missiles (GLCMs) as NATO's latest 'life insurance', helping preserve European peace. In Washington the main deterrent considered of value is the strategic one: ICBMs cannot be shot down, but GLCMs can. NATO is anxious, however, to preserve a variety of different levels

Despite its sophistication, the swing-wing supersonic Tu-26 'Backfire' bomber, like all aircraft, could be shot down.

of nuclear confrontation: although GLCMs and other tactical weapons are of questionable survivability they are retained because they are several rungs down from the top of the ladder of escalation of nuclear war towards global destruction.

Nevertheless the spectre of nuclear war hangs over NATO in Europe with the possibility that one day the Warsaw Pact countries might invade probably using (initially) conventional arms. These would be met with NATO conventional forces. It is unlikely, however, that the superiority of the Warsaw Pact forces could be overcome by NATO's conventional forces, so the nuclear initiative might be taken by the latter with the firing of a small number of tactical nuclear weapons. NATO hopes that at this stage the Soviet leaders would order a withdrawal not wishing to escalate the nuclear conflict. According to official NATO information the idea is to show the Soviets that the West is prepared to use nuclear weapons in Europe, and by so doing prevent a large-scale conflict.[3]

The question remains: what happens if this initial small-scale use of tactical nuclear weapons is unsuccessful? It seems incredible that having invaded western Europe (a decision which would not have been taken lightly) the Soviet leadership would indeed back down at this stage. From this point onwards the war could escalate, though NATO plans to match every level of escalation with opportunities for peace: their aim is to make it possible for each side to halt the war without losing too much honour (or too many million civilian and military lives) in order to prevent worse to come. NATO commanders are aware that initially crossing the 'nuclear threshold' by using just a small number of tactical weapons is a gigantic step towards global war. They know the stakes are very high, but they might be compelled to take the risk: otherwise the deterrent value of the NATO posture would not be credible and Warsaw Pact conventional forces could do as they pleased without fear of NATO reprisals.

Nuclear arsenals

The superpowers rightly consider their strategic missiles (ICBMs and SLBMs) to be of over-riding importance in the global balance of terror. No other nuclear delivery system is sufficiently invulnerable to attack to guarantee a retaliatory capacity after sustaining a full-scale attack.

ICBMs are protected in concrete silos and can only be successfully attacked by highly accurate ground-burst detonations. Even then the most optimistic predictions suggest that at least one missile in ten would survive a concerted attack. Because ICBMs are based in accurately surveyed land positions they are extremely accurate in flight, and can be used to attack small, protected targets such as other missiles. China is gradually building up an arsenal in which ICBMs feature in order to counteract the Soviet threat.

Submarine-launched missiles are also relatively invulnerable to attack. Half of the United States SLBMs and one-fifth of the Soviet Union's SLBMs are deployed at sea at any one time and cannot easily be destroyed with today's anti-submarine warfare techniques.

The calculations which indicate the numbers of such strategic systems likely to survive a first strike dictate the numbers of warheads each superpower regards as being necessary to preserve the strategic balance. A few hundred warheads could guarantee urban destruction in either country, but the 7,300 American ballistic missile strategic warheads and the 5,700 possessed by the Soviet Union guarantee overkill: the required capacity to retaliate even after a successful first strike by the other side.

The fact that the United States can deliver perhaps 2,000 warheads by strategic bomber aircraft, compared with the Soviet Union's few hundred, may not be important to the overall balance of power because adequate air defences could eliminate aircraft. Bombers would be important, however, if radar and anti-aircraft defences had been destroyed, and strategic bombers should be viewed in this light.

Although both the USSR and USA possess several thousand tactical warheads having ranges in excess of 100 miles (160 km) these are retained for quite different reasons from strategic warheads. America first deployed such weapons in

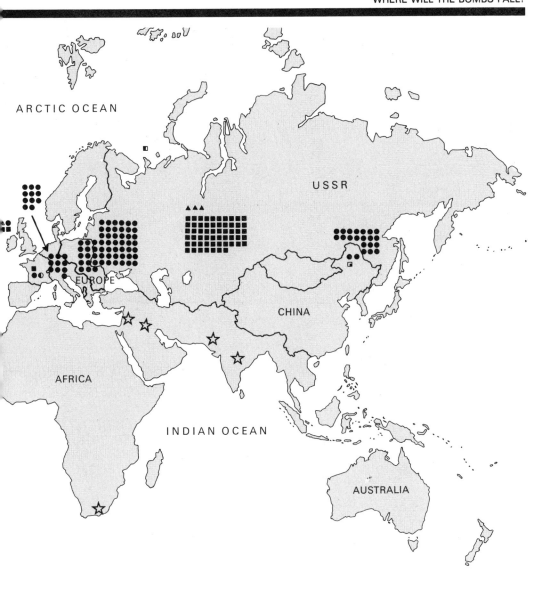

ARCTIC OCEAN

USSR

EUROPE

CHINA

AFRICA

INDIAN OCEAN

AUSTRALIA

Europe during the 1950s when their possession conferred an obvious military deterrence value in the absence of similar weapons on the Soviet side. But today both sides possess these weapons, together with perhaps even larger numbers of very short-range tactical weapons, mainly because it seems clear that no military advantage could be achieved by reducing the size of such arsenals even though the prospect of engaging in battles in which nuclear weapons are detonated at relatively close range is horrific to soldiers and civilian populations alike.

The proliferation of nuclear weapon-owning countries is a fairly recent trend and it would indeed be surprising if it did not continue.

▲ 100 strategic warheads (ICBMs)
■ 100 strategic warheads (aircraft)
● 100 tactical warheads
☆ suspected nuclear weapons

Attack against the United States

It is very unlikely that a nuclear attack would be mounted against America without a preceding conflict elsewhere such as in Europe where the superpowers already have military commitments. The Soviet Union's superiority of conventional forces suggests that nuclear weapons would be used first by American-backed forces such as NATO. In Europe NATO would be expected to be reluctant to use tactical nuclear weapons because of the risks of contaminating their own territory if the fighting took place in West Europe. But from the moment of first crossing the nuclear threshold it would be possible that a large attack might be mounted directly against the USA.

From MAD to limited nuclear war

One of the reasons that nuclear war now seems more likely than in the past is that suggestions are being made about the possibility of conducting wars which do not lead to total annihilation, but remain limited in order to have specific political effects.

On the principle of mutual assured destruction (MAD) it was accepted that both major military alliances (NATO and the Warsaw Pact) had the ability to destroy each other totally, with no guarantee, however, of avoiding total destruction at home from retaliation. Effective defence against nuclear weapons could not be guaranteed, and so the potential aggressor was assumed to be deterred by the prospect of devastation at home, and would thus never make the first move. One reason that this balance of terror came into being was because of technical limitations in nuclear weapons and their delivery systems. The accuracy of missile targeting and reliability of the weapons were so poor that protected military targets could not be attacked with any degree of certainty that they would be destroyed. The weapons were only accurate and reliable enough to be used as a threat against cities, large and sprawling enough to be vulnerable even to missiles capable of missing a target by several miles. Both sides could be reasonably sure of dispatching lethal numbers of weapons (missiles and bombs) to cause huge levels of death and destruction, but it was questionable whether military might could be subdued by such an attack. It was judged that populations at risk could urge political leaders not to engage in nuclear war, thus producing the desired 'deterrent' effect.

This has now changed totally. According to the Stockholm International Peace Research Institute (SIPRI),[4] 'there are serious grounds to fear that the concept of mutual assured destruction, with all its faults, will be abandoned in favour of a war-fighting and war-winning strategy'.

One reason for this change is that technical improvements have made nuclear weapons more effective against hard targets (ie those protected against blast) such as missiles within concrete silos. The main improvement is in targeting accuracy. There is debate about the degree of technical improvement which has taken place, but it is now thought possible that some missiles could strike within a few tens of feet of the intended target. If sufficient numbers of such highly accurate missiles could be dispatched to destroy enemy nuclear delivery systems before they could be used in retaliation, there must be a severe risk that (under extreme pressure) one side might decide to make a pre-emptive move. The more confident nuclear powers become in the reliability of their bombs and missiles the more likely is the waging of a war in which purely military targets are involved – a so-called 'counterforce' war against enemy nuclear weapons. Such wars, however, would inevitably cause a catastrophic amount of collateral destruction and slaughter of massive numbers of civilians.

Improvements in targeting

The latest cruise missiles have radar systems said to be capable of recognising precisely the terrain over which they are flying (by comparing it with a reference 'map' of ground features obtained by satellite photography and stored in the missile's computer memory) and thus striking within very close range of any target. It should be mentioned that manned bombers have been able to achieve such accuracy for many years by making use of 'computers' within

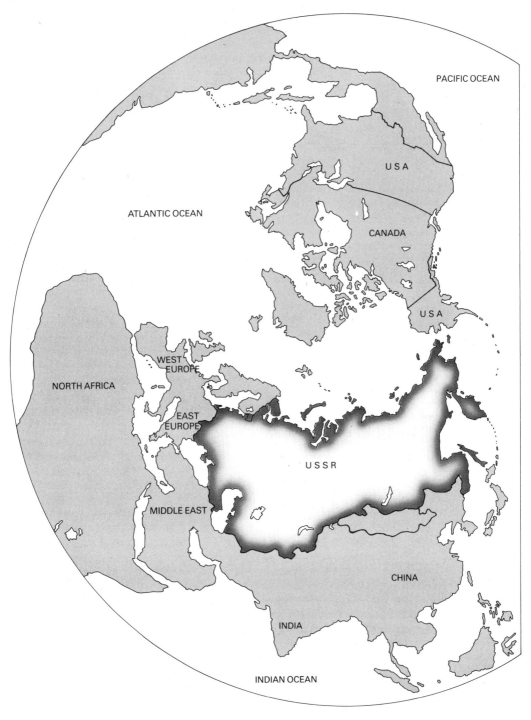

Unlike the United States, which has no unfriendly nations nearby, the world looks a threatening place from the Soviet Union: Europe on the west and China to the east add to the worries arising from the politically unstable countries south of the USSR.

57

Many thousands of nuclear warheads are deployed in Europe ready for action. The European NATO countries (Britain, France, Belgium, West Germany, Italy, Denmark, the Netherlands, Luxembourg, Norway, Portugal, Greece and Turkey) keep themselves permanently ready for war with the help of the United States) against the Warsaw Pact countries (the Soviet Union, Bulgaria, Czechoslovakia, East Germany, Hungary, Poland and Rumania). Because there is a 'cordon sanitaire' of neutral countries (Switzerland, Austria, Yugoslavia, Sweden and Finland) running through much of Europe the obvious battle zone for any future war is Germany.

Britain and France possess their own independent nuclear weapons, though in the case of Britain these are committed to joint NATO use only. Other NATO countries operate nuclear weapons supplied by the United States under 'joint key' arrangements: American approval must be given for the use of such arms.

The variety and number of nuclear warheads in Europe is immense. Mobile ballistic missiles deployed on land and at sea are capable of carrying large warheads hundreds or thousands of miles. Short-range ballistic missiles, heavy artillery firing shells containing nuclear warheads, long-range bombers and short-range strike aircraft complete the range of delivery systems.

Neutral countries

Warsaw Pact territory

NATO territory

NATO member, militarily independent

human skulls. Questions are always raised about the vulnerability of bombers and cruise missiles to attack from the ground, using surface-to-air missiles and other anti-aircraft defences. But if significant numbers can reach their targets, this could convince a potential aggressor that a successful counterforce war could be waged.

A constant fear is that improvements in weapons technology could one day make a successful first strike possible. Already several refinements have been introduced which now favour the side first 'pushing the button'.

Factors favouring first strike

1. Communication with aircraft and submarines depends on radio. Satellite

radio systems help ships, aircraft and submarines to navigate. If one nuclear power decided to attack without warning it would have the advantage of enjoying good communications with its strategic forces. Also ships, aircraft and submarines would know their positions accurately, an essential pre-requisite of bomb or missile aiming.

2. Only Very Low Frequency (VLF) and Extremely Low Frequency (ELF) broadcasts can be used to contact submarines which stay submerged continuously. These depend on the use of extremely large aerials mostly on land which are easily destroyed by missiles, so they could become useless soon after the beginning of a war. Submarines could thus become isolated from command headquarters after the outbreak of war, but if used in a first strike would be in constant communication up to the time of firing the missiles.

3. Navigation systems for vessels and aircraft can also be used to guide missiles more accurately than by inertial guidance alone – but only before the beginning of a war. After nuclear hostilities had begun satellites and ground stations could be among the first targets. So the extra accuracy conferred by the peacetime launch conditions (possible only if an attack were made without warning or provocation) would give the attacking side a supreme advantage.

4. Recent improvements in the sonar detection of submarines (by listening to the sounds they make and noting the echoes they produce) might eventually make the world's oceans 'transparent'. Submarines will no longer be undetectable, predicts SIPRI;[5] so they, along with missile silos and bomber bases could join the list of targets in a counterforce war.

A first strike therefore might well consist of a pure counterforce attack. If this does not succeed fully, second and subsequent strikes might be mounted against other targets.

Military strategies

The military commander using nuclear weapons for war-fighting (not just war-deterring) would take into consideration a huge number of different factors such as whether to use a low- or high-yield weapon, surface or air burst; whether to make use of the fallout (for example as a method of causing everyone to take shelter, from which they would not be able to fight easily for fear of radiation exposure), and which particular range and type of weapon to use. Artillery firing rounds of low-yield nuclear devices on to an opposing army 10 miles away would be used in quite different circumstances from short-range ballistic missiles (having ranges of, for example, a hundred miles or so).

With the huge variety of weapons at his or her disposal, the military commander would need to exercise great skills to win a nuclear battle, taking into consideration such possibilities as kinds of weapons systems and changes in the weather.

One fact is certain concerning the secret 'war games' continually played out by the military: colossal loss of life is assumed. The British Home Office assumes tens of millions of civilians dead as the result of a nuclear attack on Britain.[6] Military leaders presumably consider this an unavoidable consequence of nuclear war and would not allow this to deter them from trying to 'win' the conflict.

Air and surface bursts

The small battlefield bombs ('mini-nukes') of 1-kt yield or thereabouts could be used against soldiers. These can be delivered by artillery or by means of short range missiles. Armies in close combat would want to avoid fallout as much as possible: it would not kill opposing soldiers quickly enough to have any short-term military value, and it would threaten (depending on wind direction) the health of the forces dispatching the weapons. So air bursts would be preferred for most purposes.

Also, air bursts would distribute the blast overpressure more efficiently, reaching a larger area than surface bursts, and heat could radiate better giving soldiers on the ground little chance to shield themselves: taking cover behind a wall, for example, would not help if the explosion were directly overhead.

Initial radiation

Initial radiation from battlefield 'mini-nukes' would be a great risk to anybody in the target area. Half a mile beneath a 1-kt explosion people in the open might survive the 4 psi blast overpressure, and could avoid severe burns with suitable clothing, but would receive 500 r of initial radiation: more than the dose which is lethal to half the population so exposed (the LD 50 dose). So more than half of these victims would die within a month of the exposure.

For some military purposes it might be considered useful to expose enemy soldiers to initial radiation like this. At an altitude of half a mile (1 km) the air burst would produce no local fallout, so there would be little risk of being harmed by one's own weapons. This is exactly the way in which neutron bombs would be used: they would be an appealing option to a battle-commander who had encountered a pocket of resisting soldiers who did not have any nuclear weapons. Without risking his own soldiers lives by ordering a conventional attack, the commander could use small air-burst nuclear weapons to expose the enemy to radiation and then just wait for them to die.

Strategic targets

Military installations which are judged to be on the list of target priorities are normally well protected. Aircraft not in use are kept in hardened hangers – ones made from reinforced concrete able to withstand blast overpressures from nuclear explosions quite nearby, perhaps as close as a mile or so. Cruise missiles would be stored in similar hardened sheds, buried where possible and well camouflaged. Command headquarters and emergency government offices are buried deep underground and are among the 'hardest' of all military targets. Land-based ICBMs are kept in reinforced concrete silos which could withstand very close nuclear strikes, say a quarter of a mile from a 1-Mt explosion.

High air-burst weapons would be useless against ICBM silos. Only by detonating weapons on, or just above, the ground accurately on target could such installations be destroyed. Aircraft hangers and cruise missile stores might be destroyed by surface-burst weapons. Only earth-penetrating multi-megaton warheads would have a chance of destroying deep underground command bunkers. So a war against hardened military targets implies the use of moderate and high-yield surface-burst weapons and hence would lead to massive fallout.

Multiple strikes

Hardened targets might often be allocated several warheads each to increase the chance of their being destroyed. A single warhead on a single hardened target has a high statistical chance of destroying the target. For the most accurate modern strategic weapons this probability of a 'kill' could be as high as 90 per cent.[7] But even if two weapons were used there would be a small chance that the target would survive the attack.[8] It is the tiny chance of survival which allows a thread of uncertainty to remain in military minds, but as the warheads become more accurate and reliable the uncertainty decreases. The American MX mobile missile system (see page 25) is a means of increasing the uncertainty by making sure the enemy would never know the precise locations of land-based missiles. Because none of the weapons has been tried out in actual war conditions there is intrinsic uncertainty in nuclear war-fighting because technological faults and equipment malfunctions (along with all the unpredictable weapon effects) will always be present. This is one reason why opponents of the expensive MX system believe it is unnecessary.

Target priorities

To get some idea of which targets might be attacked in a nuclear strike against America it is necessary to consider what the military aims of the Soviet Union might be and how they would best achieve them.

In the European theatre NATO believes

in the use of a 'token strike', a limited nuclear offensive which would teach the other side that they meant business. The enemy would be expected to withdraw from action or hurry to the negotiating table as a result of such a strike. If the Soviet Union wished to make a token strike against the United States it might choose to do as much economic damage as possible with a very limited number of warheads. As Americans are aware of the large number of warheads in the entire Soviet arsenal the vast destruction caused by just a few would certainly make the point very strongly. The Soviet Union would hope that America (and the rest of NATO, which might get the same treatment) would negotiate for peace.

Oil refineries are very tempting targets for the purpose of causing great economic damage without escalating the nuclear attack to a high level. Other energy production facilities could also be targeted for the same purpose. It is possible that a lower level of attack might be mounted against any of a wide range of industrial targets purely to give an example of the levels of damage which could follow if the country did not agree to negotiate.

One of the most likely patterns of attack, however, is the limited counterforce attack against missiles, nuclear weapons dumps, bombers and their bases and submarine bases. Such an attack aims to disarm the opponent making retaliation more difficult. In fact the growth of overkill ensures *some* retaliatory capacity, but as nuclear war might only begin in desperate political conditions the ability to eliminate some of the other side's nuclear war-fighting capacity might be a good enough aim. So any nuclear weapon on American soil is fundamentally a counterforce target.

Extending the principle of attacking a nation's war-fighting capacity, next on the list of target priorities could be all military installations (including communications systems such as early warning radar, VLF masts and satellite ground stations).

Ports and airports would also be important to the fighting of a theatre war, such as a protracted campaign in Europe. These might be targeted to make it more difficult for NATO to send re-inforcements and supplies to the European battlefields.

In a full scale attack, all military targets, ports and airfields, and economic targets such as oil refineries might be attacked, but a variety of industrial centres could also be considered important targets: by destroying a General Motors truck production line, for example, America's recovery after an attack would be slowed. In practice these industrial targets lie close to cities, and the attack pattern for a full scale strike against the United States would include a bomb for almost every city.

Bearing these plausible military aims in mind a study by the US Office of Technology Assessment[9] considers four distinct attack patterns which represent the range of possibilities:

1. An attack against a single city.
2. A limited attack, using a specified number of warheads, on targets important to the economic activity of the country.
3. A counterforce attack on such targets as missiles, bomber bases and submarine bases.
4. A full scale attack, including military, economic and industrial targets, with populations not being directly targeted.

The attack against a single city is included because it would inevitably become part of Case 4 where industrial targets lie within cities. These hypothetical attacks might be quite different from an actual attack pattern, but by studying them it is possible to understand the range of effects if there were a nuclear war.

Case 2 describes an attack against energy production which might be plausible if the Soviet Union wanted to demonstrate the extreme extent of economic damage which could be inflicted by a very limited number of warheads. This case study is conceived as a typical 'bargaining chip' which might be used to win a war without causing escalation and extreme devastation.

One of the most interesting possibilities is that discussed in Case 3 because of the view held by many observers that a counterforce attack is the 'least irrational way of waging nuclear war'. Certainly now that missiles have become more accurate, there seems to be little point in continuing with the 'balance of terror' on which the MAD policies of the past have been based. Why fire at cities when missiles, bomber bases, submarine bases and other nuclear delivery systems could be attacked?

Estimates of weapons available for use against the United States have been published in *The Military Balance*,[10] and it can be assumed that a suitable fraction of this arsenal could be used against America.

General assumptions
1. The entire ICBM force of the Soviet Union would be available for use against the United States.
2. No Soviet aircraft would be allocated for use against the American mainland.
3. No sea-launched cruise missiles would be used against land-based targets.
4. One-fifth of Russia's SLBMs (those normally on submarines at sea) could be allocated to attacks against America.
5. No invasion takes place, hence no nuclear artillery or other tactical nuclear weapon can be used in America.

There might be a further reduction in the numbers of delivery systems which could be mounted for North American action because some would be out of service for routine maintenance or repairs. Nuclear missiles are far from perfect examples of technology. They are exceedingly complex, susceptible to breakdowns like any other machine and, of course, have never been tested in actual combat conditions.

Numbers of warheads
According to the estimates published in *The Military Balance* the Soviet Union has about 5,700 strategic warheads available for delivery by intercontinental or submarine-launched ballistic missile. Nearly 1,000 of these Soviet ballistic missiles are submarine-launched, and these carry about 1,500 warheads. As only about 20 per cent of Soviet submarines are normally at sea (and a sudden departure from home base by a larger proportion of the submarine fleet would signal a possible attack

and lose any element of surprise) it is reasonable to assume that there would be only about 300 warheads available from SLBMs. The total number of strategic warheads available for an attack on America would thus be about 4,500. On the optimistic assumption that 90 per cent of such warheads would be serviceable at the time of the attack the number of warheads available works out at just over 4,000.

The assumptions about which warheads are practically available for use against America, and the count of warheads are included to give a realistic impression of the *scale* of possible attacks. It is possible, but less likely, that more than 4,000 warheads could be used simultaneously in an all-out attack against the United States: the results would be enormously devastating.

Typical warhead yields would be 2-Mt from the SS-18 missiles carrying multiple warheads, a small number of high-yield (more than 18-Mt) warheads from SS-18s fitted with single warheads, 550-kt warheads from MIRVed SS-19 ICBMs, and 1-Mt warheads from missiles such as the submarine-launched SS-N-12 and the ageing but plentiful SS-11 ICBM.

In fact hardly any targets would be worth using the biggest warheads (18 to 25-Mt) in the Soviet Union's arsenal. In the past these were deployed because their massive blast could compensate for inaccuracies in targeting. It is now believed that Soviet ICBMs are as accurate as their American counterparts, and provided good targeting accuracy is achieved one megaton or thereabouts is sufficient to destroy any likely target.

All at once?
It is not enough to say, however, that 4,000 bombs could reach America: the questions remain as to whether *all* warheads would be used in a *single* attack within minutes or hours of each other, or whether the attack would be spread over a period of time, or whether it would be confined to specific categories of targets only. Nevertheless the specific case studies which follow illustrate the magnitude of the possible devastation resulting from the various assumed types of attack.

Case 1 *Attack on a single city*

The San Francisco Bay Area is a typical city region which could be targeted in some of the least likely but nevertheless plausible attack strategies. Hypothetical single-bomb attacks have been studied for Detroit, USA, and Leningrad in the USSR[11], both of which have populations of about four millions, roughly comparable with the numbers of people living in San Francisco, Oakland and Berkeley. Although the Bay Area topography is different from that of either Detroit or Leningrad it is justifiable to assume similar levels of devastation and casualties. This is because the blast wave produced by a nuclear explosion would hug the surface, travelling over and around San Francisco's hills.

The consequences could vary considerably depending on the time of day or night, the weather, amount of warning time, the availability of help from elsewhere, and other factors which cannot be predicted. To simplify the calculations we assume:

1. There is no warning, hence the population would neither evacuate nor shelter.
2. The attack is at night when people are mostly at home.
3. There is clear visibility.
4. No other cities are attacked, so outside help could be available.

Explosion at the US Naval Shipyard
If a 1-Mt device exploded on the ground at the Naval Shipyard, Hunters Point (about 7 miles (11 km) north of San Francisco International Airport), someone 10 miles (16 km) to the north-east, in Berkeley, for example, would find the darkness of night suddenly transformed into brilliant light, far brighter than daytime. Looking at the fireball would cause flashblindness or even permanent loss of sight through severe retinal burns (made worse by the eye's adaptation to the low light levels of night time).

The blast accompanied by a rush of wind would follow nearly one minute after the brilliant flash, breaking windows and even some doors in the Berkeley area. Minutes later the moon and stars would be blotted

out by a growing mushroom cloud spreading over the central Bay Area. There would be an eerie silence, broken by the crackle of flames and the crash of falling debris and masonry, particularly from the San Francisco direction. Soon a bright red glow would replace the darkness, lighting everywhere despite the loss of street lamps. This would be caused by the fiercely blazing ruins of the western half of down-town San Francisco, reaching perhaps as far as Golden Gate Park about 8 miles (13 km) away.

Survivors would have to tune their radios to out of town broadcasting stations as both local radio and television stations might be off the air. If it were confirmed that the attack was an isolated one, the nation would immediately leap to San Francisco's assistance. But there would be an intensely radioactive cloud of fallout dust to contend with. In Berkeley anybody staying outside for a few hours soon after the explosion might receive a lethal dose of fallout radiation (if south-westerly winds were blowing at the time of explosion). A huge band of country could be made lethally radioactive for a few weeks, and people would have to take shelter or remove themselves from the advancing path of the deadly dust before it arrived. It would be difficult to evacuate to a safer area, however, as the wind might change direction. Also some places might receive extremely large amounts of fallout because of rainfall. Fear of fallout would greatly hinder rescue operations.

The Naval Shipyard itself would be totally devastated and replaced by a crater 1,000 feet (300 m) wide and about 200 feet (60 m) deep, which would probably fill with sea water. Candlestick Park, home of the San Francisco Giants, and the Bayview district would be destroyed beyond all recognition. Any fires started by the initial flash in this region might be rapidly blown out by the blast.

St Lukes and San Francisco Hospitals, 3 miles (5 km) from ground zero, would be destroyed along with most of their occupants. This highlights one further problem: hospitals would not be able to cope

Anyone witnessing the growth of a huge fireball over the Naval Shipyard might believe the end of the world had come. In seconds the heart of a modern city would be erased. Although such destruction would achieve little the threat is made today to deter war. If such deterrence breaks down, however, cities would be obliterated in unrestrained nuclear retaliation.

with all the casualties. There could be several hundred thousand severe burns victims and a similar number with fractures, severe lacerations and haemorrhage. Many of these could survive with hospital care, but with local hospitals reduced to rubble little treatment could be given. Not even the entire national health resources of clinics, hospitals and medical personnel could cope with an emergency of such magnitude, with perhaps only 1,000 to 2,000 intensive-care beds in the whole of America available for specialist treatment of severe burns. Because medical facilities would be completely swamped, many victims would die painfully without treatment.

The death toll could reach several hundred thousand after four weeks, and could double over the following few months as the delayed effects of injuries and radiation sickness took effect. Most of the casualties would come from within a circle of 5-miles (8-km) radius, reaching parts of Alameda across San Francisco Bay and Daly City towards the Pacific coast where practically all buildings would be flattened by the blast and also razed by fire. Deaths from fallout could occur as far as Sacramento, 80 miles (130 km) away and even beyond (with south-westerly winds).

An air burst of the same weapon would increase the circle of devastation to include most of Berkeley, Oakland and San Francisco's Airport 7 or 8 miles (11 or 13 km) away. Twice as many people would die from blast and heat effects, but there would be no fallout.

25-Mt air burst over San Francisco

The effect of a 25-Mt explosion in the air above the Bay Area would be staggering: almost total destruction of buildings within a range of 20 miles (32 km), including places as far as San Rafael (to the north) and Menlo Park (to the south). Allowing for the greater population of this huge area of devastation there could be more than two million people killed either instantaneously or within 30 days, and many more with injuries severe enough to threaten life later than this. Anybody exposed to the flash within this 20-mile (32-km) radius would receive third degree burns on exposed skin, and fires would start everywhere and possibly build up into massive conflagrations or even fire storms. Every window in San Jose more than 30 miles (48 km) away, would be shattered, and a powerful wind, nearly 40 mph (64 km/h), would be felt blowing from the San Francisco direction. The explosion would be heard all over California.

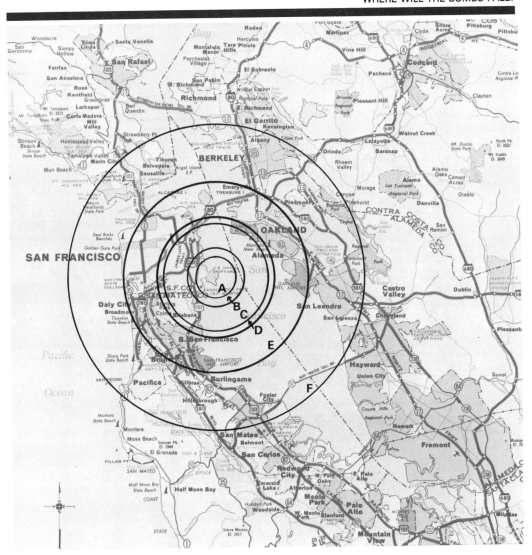

1 inch = approx 8 miles
2.5 cm = approx 12.8 km

The entire area within ring (E), 8 miles (13 km) from the Naval Shipyard, could become a fire zone, causing huge numbers of casualties among San Francisco's population. Complete fire devastation and blast destruction would be almost certain between ring (B) – 2.5 miles (4 km) from ground zero – and ring (D) – 5 miles (8 km) away. Although most fires inside (B) would probably be extinguished by blast winds it would be of little comfort to the inhabitants who would be blasted to pieces. No building would remain standing within

ring (A) – 1.6 miles (2.5 km) from the explosion – and about 10 per cent of structures would be destroyed out to ring (E), including perhaps San Francisco's famous Golden Gate bridge. All the windows and many doors at the University of California, Berkeley, would be broken as would other thin structures out to ring (F) – 13 miles (20 km) away. Even beyond, as far south as Palo Alto, it would be unlikely if there were any unbroken windows.

Case 2 *Limited attack against refineries*

The assumption is that the maximum loss of oil-refining capacity should be inflicted from the use of only ten missiles, carrying 80 warheads, without deliberately trying to minimise human casualties. In the emergency conditions of approaching hostilities, such nuclear war-fighting strategies might reluctantly be adopted as necessary by the Soviet Union as a means of convincing the United States of their resolve to fight a nuclear war. If America went to the negotiating table rather than retaliating it would prove that the theory of deterrence works in practice – it is of interest to note, however, the results of obtaining such proof.

The hypothetical attack is mounted against oil refining, rather than any other sector of the American economy, because this causes the most serious and long-term economic damage within the limitation of using only ten missiles. If the SS-18 ICBM was used this could deliver ten clusters of eight warheads on each of ten areas of American soil. US oil refineries are (conveniently for the purposes of this attack) clustered together. Results published in *The Effects of Nuclear War*[12] show that nearly 64 per cent of US refining capacity would be lost by such a successful strike. The aggressor would probably intend that the missiles should explode in the air, to cause maximum blast damage. Some, however, might accidentally detonate on the ground producing huge amounts of fallout. In any event the population would have no information before the attack about whether the weapons would produce fallout or not, so, if they had sufficient warning, they would have to prepare themselves for the possibility of fallout. The massive public disturbance created from war preparations (not to mention mass attempts at evacuation, probably frustrated by blocked roads, sheer panic and government restrictions) would inflict their own dire consequences. The old, young children and the infirm, would all suffer most in the panic. A mad scramble for protection and shelter could result in the 'survival of the fittest', with many casualties suffering from the desperate, fearful

◆ oil refinery

actions of other citizens. For many people, the consequences would be intolerable. Bereavement would be commonplace, all self-confidence and optimism could be destroyed, mental breakdowns might be frequent – so would suicide and severe depression. Anger and resentment could soon arise and lead to crime, rioting, civil disorder and chaos. The psychological effect on the American civilian population, which sustained no deaths during the Second World War and could, following this limited attack, be left with several millions dead or dying, cannot be assessed.

Yet all these consequences are 'side effects' of the main purpose of the attack.

1 Linden, NJ
2 Perth Amboy, NJ
3 Paulsboro, NJ
4 Philadelphia, Pa
5 Marcus Hook, Pa
   (2 refineries)
6 Westville, NJ
7 Delaware City, Del
8 Toledo, Oh
   (2 refineries)
9 Lima, Oh
10 Whiting, Ind
11 Joliett, Ill
12 Cattletsburg, Ky*
13 Lawrenceville, Ill
14 Wood River, Ill
   (2 refineries)
15 Sugar Creek, Mo
16 Eldorado, Ka
17 Kansas City, Ka
18 Ponco City, Ok
19 Borger, Tx*
20 Robinson, Tx
21 Pasagoula, Ms
22 Garyville, La
23 Convenient, La
24 Belle Chasse, La
25 Norco, La

26 Baton Rouge, La
27 Mereux, La
28 West Lake, La
29 Port Arthur, Tx
   (3 refineries)
30 Beaumont, Tx
31 Deer Park, Tx
32 Lemont, Tx
33 Nederland, Tx
34 Texas City, Tx
35 Houston, Tx
36 Sweeny, Tx
37 Corpus Christi, Tx
   (3 refineries)
38 El Paso, Tx*
39 Benicia, Ca
40 Martinez, Ca
41 Richmond, Ca
42 Carson, Ca
43 El Segundo, Ca
44 Torrence, Ca
45 Wilmington, Ca
   (3 refineries)
46 Avon, Ca

*these refineries not
targeted in this attack

About two-thirds of America's refining capacity could be destroyed with disastrous consequences for industry, transport and patterns of work spreading over the ensuing months and years.

Loss of oil-refining facilities and the country's bulk supplies would lead to serious setbacks for industry. Even with a third of refining capacity remaining, not all industries would get their share because the Government might have to ration scarce resources. The plastics, clothing, agricultural chemicals, paint and other industries using petroleum products could cease for months or even years. Obviously transport would be affected, but the lack of oil would also cause widespread domestic problems. People would not be able to get to work even to do jobs which did not rely on oil. There could be food shortages. And the country could face huge debts as it attempted to purchase emergency stocks and rebuild the damaged oil facilities. In short: this very limited form of attack, not deliberately intended to harm the civilian population (the sort of attack we could be persuaded should be launched against an enemy for the purpose of protecting *our* homeland) would cause immense, possibly irrevocable, devastation. And yet only a total of 80 warheads of the available arsenal of 4,000 would have been used.

Case 3 *Limited counterforce attack*

A counterforce attack on the USA could be mounted against bomber and submarine bases and the known and suspected locations of missiles. It is assumed for the purposes of this limited calculation that the aim would be to cripple America's ability to retaliate by destroying most of her nuclear weapons on the ground, striking a decisive blow which would help win the war.

A counterforce attack would necessarily be a large one, with two warheads allocated to each of America's 1054 ICBM silos in the nine missile fields: two in North Dakota, one in each of Arizona, South Dakota, Arkansas, Montana, Kansas and Missouri, and one on the corner where Colorado, Nebraska and Wyoming meet. Submarine support bases such as Charleston (South Carolina), and Strategic Air Command bases including Wrightson (New Jersey), Rome (New York), Limestone (Maine) and Sacramento (California), would be essential targets for the purpose of disarming the United States to limit retaliation: the accepted rationale for a counterforce attack. The complete list would include secret arms dumps so the pattern of attack must remain in some doubt.

To achieve a 'surgical strike' (to borrow jargon from the Vietnam War), the smallest and most accurate warheads might be used. These would consist principally of the multiple-warhead versions of the SS-17 (four 900-kt warheads), the SS-18 (eight 600-kt warheads) and the SS-19 (six 550-kt warheads). The intention might be to minimise the bomb effects on areas of population while destroying the military targets. To achieve this, however, many ground bursts, necessary to destroy hardened missile silos, would have to be used, causing massive amounts of fallout.

To attack airborne bombers which would scramble within minutes of an attack warning, a systematic blanket of air-burst detonations could be used by the attacker to destroy all air traffic within a calculated volume of air space.

In studies of such a counterforce attack on the United States mainland,[13] it has been variously estimated that between one

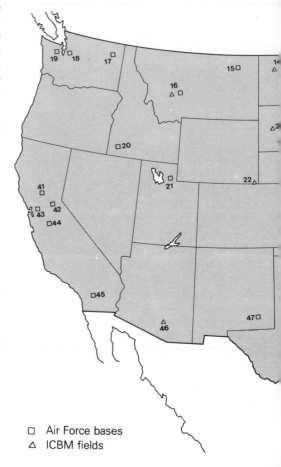

□ Air Force bases
△ ICBM fields

and ten per cent of civilians could lose their lives from the immediate and short-term effects of the explosions, with more dying later from the wide range of delayed effects. It is not possible to calculate more accurately than this the number of likely casualties in a counterforce attack, because of the many variables – weapon design, height of burst, wind, rain, terrain, targeting accuracy and so on.

Only the most optimistic assumptions could reduce casualty estimates below five per cent: more than ten million people. Many would die from blast and heat because the bases attacked are relatively close to urban areas. This illustrates the impossi-

1 Limestone, Me
2 Portsmith, NH
3 Chicopee, Mass
4 Plattsburg, NY
5 Rome, NY
6 Wrightson, NJ
7 Columbus, Oh
8 Dayton, Oh
9 Grissom, Peru, Ind
10 Oscoda, Mi
11 Gwinn, Mi
12 Kincheloe, Mi
13 Grand Forks, ND
14 Minot, ND
15 Glasgow, Mt
16 Great Falls, Mt
17 Victorville, Wa
18 Tacombe, Wa
19 Bangar, Wa
20 Mountain Home, Id
21 Ogden, Ut
22 Warren, Wy
23 Ellsworth, SD
24 Rapid City, SD
25 Goldsboro, NC
26 Charleston, SC
27 Macon, Ga
28 Orlando, Fl

29 Tampa, Fl
30 Homestead, Fl
31 Columbus, Ms
32 Blytheville, Ar
33 Pine Bluff, Ar
34 Little Rock, Ar
35 Belton, Mo
36 Whiteman, Mo
37 McConnel, Ks
38 Wichita, Ks
39 Beltow, Ks
40 Junction City, Ks
41 Marysville, Ca
42 Sacramento, Ca
43 Fairfield, Ca
44 Merced, Ca
45 San Bernardino, Ca
46 Davis-Monthan, Az
47 Albuquerque, NM
48 Amarillo, Tx
49 Enid, Ok
50 Altus, Ok
51 Fort Worth, Tx
52 Abilene, Tx
53 Austin, Tx
54 San Antonio, Tx
55 Shreveport, La

bility of mounting a pure 'counterforce' attack which strikes weapons but not people: in practice any such 'limited nuclear war' strategy would kill millions of civilians.

At least 2,000 warheads would have to be ground burst in the attempt to destroy 'hardened' silos or structures and others might detonate on the ground by accident. Intensely radioactive plumes of fallout ashes could blanket almost every part of the country, although if there were a constant wind from the west, many coastal areas not close to targets could escape contamination. Survival would depend on sheltering from the radiation, but as almost no preparations have been made by the Government to protect the population, sheltering conditions would be crude for most people and normal services would cease to exist.

Any one of the effects of such a large attack (such as the millions of deaths, massive fire storms and conflagrations, a lethal blanket of radiation, or blast destruction) could cause repercussions from which the country would take many years to recover. But *together* these effects would be unimaginably severe, posing the real threat of the permanent loss of many industries, the long-term devastation of agricultural land and disintegration of systems of government, command, welfare and education.

Case 4 Large-scale attack

If an available arsenal of some 4,000 warheads were to be launched against America, it is clear from the previous descriptions that the future existence of civilisation in America would be seriously in question.

This fourth hypothetical attack could include all military targets, notably those listed as counterforce, industrial targets such as car and truck production lines, energy supply systems including oil refineries, gas and oil pipelines, oil rigs and wells, coal mines, uranium processing facilities (which could release huge quantities of long-lived radioisotopes), centres of business and government, civilian airfields, ports, roads, railways and telecommunications installations.

The targets in such a list would inevitably lie within areas of dense population. As we have seen, in an attack on counterforce targets alone, many thousands, perhaps millions, of fatalities could result from fallout. Fallout could be even more severe in an all-out attack, but tens of millions (perhaps the majority of the population) could die from the blast, heat and other short-term effects.

The Effects of Nuclear War concludes that 77 per cent of the American population could die within 30 days from a large-scale attack: up to 165 million people.[14] Civil defence organisation and individual preparations, including evacuation and good fallout sheltering could reduce this figure, perhaps considerably. Even so, the survivors would face a precarious future, having to evade the long-term effects of fallout, devastation, complete loss of industries, international tension and perhaps even continued warfare, for there is no guarantee that a single massive nuclear exchange would end hostilities. Many of the survivors would themselves soon succumb to illness, starvation and a breakdown of communities.

An additional and very serious problem might remain for the small number of survivors of this large-scale attack: 'How could the war be brought to an end?' If communications between government com-

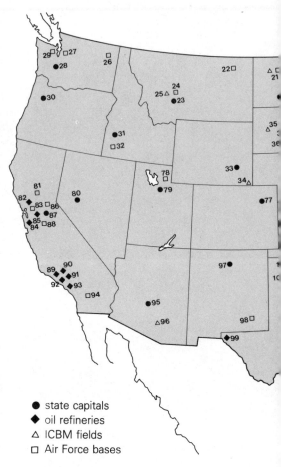

● state capitals
◆ oil refineries
△ ICBM fields
□ Air Force bases

mand and the military were disintegrated it would prove difficult to negotiate peace. If the President and deputies were among the dead or were missing it would be difficult for the enemy to know how to achieve a negotiated settlement. Isolated military units including soldiers with tactical nuclear weapons and even submarine commanders with MIRVed missiles might still be able to dispatch their deadly weapons. If warheads continued to reach America many rescue operations could be thwarted. Survivors would huddle together, dying slowly in terror, not knowing whether at any moment their agonised suffering might swiftly be ended by the arrival of yet another warhead.

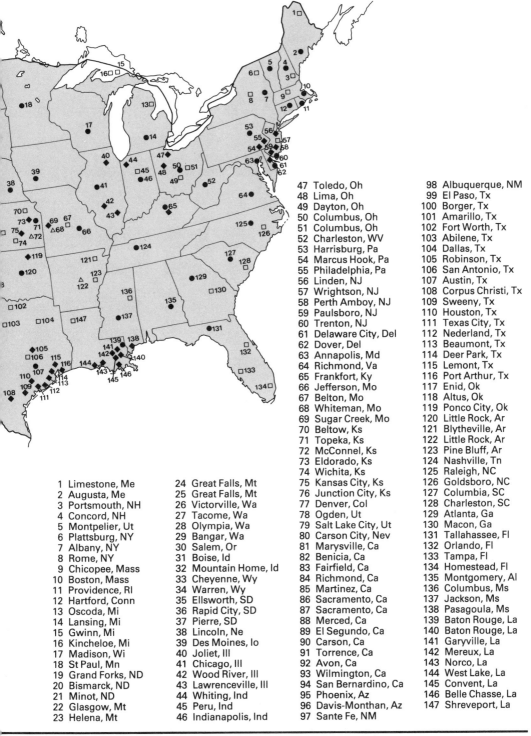

47 Toledo, Oh
48 Lima, Oh
49 Dayton, Oh
50 Columbus, Oh
51 Columbus, Oh
52 Charleston, WV
53 Harrisburg, Pa
54 Marcus Hook, Pa
55 Philadelphia, Pa
56 Linden, NJ
57 Wrightson, NJ
58 Perth Amboy, NJ
59 Paulsboro, NJ
60 Trenton, NJ
61 Delaware City, Del
62 Dover, Del
63 Annapolis, Md
64 Richmond, Va
65 Frankfort, Ky
66 Jefferson, Mo
67 Belton, Mo
68 Whiteman, Mo
69 Sugar Creek, Mo
70 Beltow, Ks
71 Topeka, Ks
72 McConnel, Ks
73 Eldorado, Ks
74 Wichita, Ks
75 Kansas City, Ks
76 Junction City, Ks
77 Denver, Col
78 Ogden, Ut
79 Salt Lake City, Ut
80 Carson City, Nev
81 Marysville, Ca
82 Benicia, Ca
83 Fairfield, Ca
84 Richmond, Ca
85 Martinez, Ca
86 Sacramento, Ca
87 Sacramento, Ca
88 Merced, Ca
89 El Segundo, Ca
90 Carson, Ca
91 Torrence, Ca
92 Avon, Ca
93 Wilmington, Ca
94 San Bernardino, Ca
95 Phoenix, Az
96 Davis-Monthan, Az
97 Sante Fe, NM

98 Albuquerque, NM
99 El Paso, Tx
100 Borger, Tx
101 Amarillo, Tx
102 Fort Worth, Tx
103 Abilene, Tx
104 Dallas, Tx
105 Robinson, Tx
106 San Antonio, Tx
107 Austin, Tx
108 Corpus Christi, Tx
109 Sweeny, Tx
110 Houston, Tx
111 Texas City, Tx
112 Nederland, Tx
113 Beaumont, Tx
114 Deer Park, Tx
115 Lemont, Tx
116 Port Arthur, Tx
117 Enid, Ok
118 Altus, Ok
119 Ponco City, Ok
120 Little Rock, Ar
121 Blytheville, Ar
122 Little Rock, Ar
123 Pine Bluff, Ar
124 Nashville, Tn
125 Raleigh, NC
126 Goldsboro, NC
127 Columbia, SC
128 Charleston, SC
129 Atlanta, Ga
130 Macon, Ga
131 Tallahassee, Fl
132 Orlando, Fl
133 Tampa, Fl
134 Homestead, Fl
135 Montgomery, Al
136 Columbus, Ms
137 Jackson, Ms
138 Pasagoula, Ms
139 Baton Rouge, La
140 Baton Rouge, La
141 Garyville, La
142 Mereux, La
143 Norco, La
144 West Lake, La
145 Convent, La
146 Belle Chasse, La
147 Shreveport, La

1 Limestone, Me
2 Augusta, Me
3 Portsmouth, NH
4 Concord, NH
5 Montpelier, Ut
6 Plattsburg, NY
7 Albany, NY
8 Rome, NY
9 Chicopee, Mass
10 Boston, Mass
11 Providence, RI
12 Hartford, Conn
13 Oscoda, Mi
14 Lansing, Mi
15 Gwinn, Mi
16 Kincheloe, Mi
17 Madison, Wi
18 St Paul, Mn
19 Grand Forks, ND
20 Bismarck, ND
21 Minot, ND
22 Glasgow, Mt
23 Helena, Mt

24 Great Falls, Mt
25 Great Falls, Mt
26 Victorville, Wa
27 Tacome, Wa
28 Olympia, Wa
29 Bangar, Wa
30 Salem, Or
31 Boise, Id
32 Mountain Home, Id
33 Cheyenne, Wy
34 Warren, Wy
35 Ellsworth, SD
36 Rapid City, SD
37 Pierre, SD
38 Lincoln, Ne
39 Des Moines, Io
40 Joliet, Ill
41 Chicago, Ill
42 Wood River, Ill
43 Lawrenceville, Ill
44 Whiting, Ind
45 Peru, Ind
46 Indianapolis, Ind

5 Protecting yourself

Public fears about the likelihood of nuclear war are rising. Interest in shelters which might protect people against the effects of near-miss nuclear explosions clearly follows. It is widely publicised that Switzerland, for example, has 'shelters for everybody' and many people believe that because of this Switzerland could take any amount of nuclear punishment and emerge with most of the population alive and ready to resume life as normal.

Shelters can be effective and could save lives but there are problems. Obviously you would have to be inside the shelter if it were to be of any use, and this could prove difficult if there were no more than a few minutes' warning of nuclear attack. Secondly, a shelter could only protect you for a limited time: the usual recommended 'shelter period' is two weeks. Unfortunately many of the problems which would probably arise in the aftermath of a nuclear strike might be even more severe after two weeks than immediately after the attack.

Effective shelters are necessarily very costly. You could only get good protection by having the shelter buried under at least three feet of earth, so to construct an effective purpose-built shelter to proper engineering standards would inevitably cost a great deal.

If there were no national policy to build shelters but you nevertheless decided to spend a large sum of money installing your own, you might find yourself in the embarrassingly privileged position after an attack of being the only person or group in your district with a shelter. With suffering all around you it might be difficult to maintain your superior short-term survival capability.

This is not to say that civil defence does not offer the hope of saving lives: it does. Shelters could keep people alive in areas on the fringes of destruction, but a shelter-building programme which offered good medium- and long-term protection for every member of the population could cost a great deal more than a nuclear arsenal. Yet, as we have seen in Chapter 4, most people might either be in the centres of blast destruction or, by chance, far away from nuclear explosions. Only a minority would have any need for shelters, so only a small proportion of shelters might benefit their owners, and even then only for a very short period of time. Evacuation to the countryside would help reduce the risk of being killed by immediate bomb effects. But knowing that your home was in such a target area, would you crawl into your shelter and risk not being able to get out again (if the house collapsed) or being suffocated by an inferno raging above? If you decided to use the shelter you might not survive the claustrophobic, filthy shelter conditions; or if you did, you might have been exposed to radiation and might not live for long once you emerged into an altered world.

Nobody should spend money on nuclear shelters without thinking of all the ramifications. For some people, possession of a shelter might serve as a morale-booster (perhaps making them more 'warlike') but as little else. Properly designed shelters can, in theory, protect people in the short and medium term from many of the effects of nuclear weapons. But the physical and psychological stress on the surviving community as a whole might easily prove so damaging that individual shelter arrangements would be totally inadequate to mitigate consequences of the catastrophe. The devastation and loss of life resulting from even the most limited attack would be far outside the experience of most people, so that assessing the value of any sheltering policy is uncertain and difficult. Very often in the literature issued by governments and by commercial companies who build shelters the immediate effects of a nuclear explosion, including local fallout, are taken into account but anything more long term than a two-week 'shelter period' is left undiscussed. Yet the combined effects of hostilities and, as we have seen in the previous chapter, the broader ramifications of even very limited nuclear strikes raise serious doubts about the value of any protective arrangements except those which take an extremely long-term view.

Civil defence

The desirability of government-organised sheltering and other civil defence measures to protect the population against nuclear attack and the extent to which they should be developed is controversial. Although shelters which protect against blast, fallout or both could save lives in the short term, the building of them on a government's instructions might be considered an aggressive act by a potential enemy. And if people became convinced that they were adequately provided with shelters they might be more easily persuaded that nuclear war was 'thinkable' and 'survivable'. So the building of shelters in a nuclear-armed nation *could* make nuclear war more likely. In fact it is doubtful whether any level of practically obtainable sheltering could save populations from the many effects of nuclear war, so the need for civil defence is by no means proven. Organised civil defence is also very costly and would be a severe drain on any country's national economy. The cost of providing the entire

population with fallout protection for a two-week shelter period would be very high indeed. Blast shelters, or protected accommodation for longer term use would cost very much more.

It would be far cheaper to attack than to defend in nuclear war, especially as no conceivable level of protection could give guarantees of survival. In view of this, together with the risk of provoking attack, it is futile in most countries to expect significant government-backed protection against nuclear attack.

In wealthy countries which do not possess nuclear weapons, however, it would be entirely reasonable to build publicly-funded blast and fallout shelters. Countries such as Switzerland, Sweden and Finland do not make any nuclear threats, so they could reasonably hope to be further down the list of target priorities than nuclear-armed nations. The blast and fallout shelters, together with extensive underground facilities which could make it possible to run the nation after an attack, significantly improve the chances of short-term survival. Rebuilding any of these countries after an attack would, despite these facilities, present tremendous (perhaps insurmountable) difficulties. The provision of shelters for the people of non-nuclear nations could not be construed as an aggressive act and they could genuinely help keep people alive at least for the first few weeks after a nuclear attack.

How much preparation?

So just how much preparation should you reasonably undertake yourself? This is a purely individual decision: if you are very worried about the threat of nuclear war, then you might feel better if you do something. It is vitally important, however, that any preparations should be made with a few points firmly in mind. There is little point in building the best shelter in the world at home if you live near a military air base, arms depot or any other obvious target. And wherever you built your protective shelter, if you got very little warning of an attack, you might not have enough time to get to it anyway.

Evacuation

It is a very natural human reaction to want to run away from danger. Many countries including the Soviet Union and the United States have prepared extensive plans for the organised evacuation of possible target areas. But in practice there are so many problems with large-scale evacuation that it is difficult to foresee a government actually giving the order to begin it. Politically, evacuation could be considered an aggressive act: the potential enemy would certainly interpret mass evacuation as preparation for nuclear war and might be tempted to strike sooner rather than engage in discussions and negotiations. Evacuation on the scale necessary would be hugely disruptive: people would have to move far away from places of work so industrial output would fall or cease altogether. Education, health services and all community activities would be curtailed and restoring them after evacuation would be both costly and lengthy. There are also great uncertainties about whether some places would be safer than others. If cities were not attacked it is possible that people would be able to shelter from fallout better at home, near to people they know, rather than in unfamiliar, possibly unfriendly or even hostile, surroundings.

Target areas

Most governments, then, could understandably be reluctant to order evacuation. Individuals on the other hand might decide to evacuate. If you believed a nuclear strike was imminent you would be wise to do so if you were in a high risk target area.

If you live close to a missile silo or store, a bomber or a submarine base (such counterforce targets are the most likely ones in an initial strike) you would be in a likely target zone, as would anybody living near a military base of any significant size. As mentioned in Chapter 4, oil refineries and pipe-lines, coal mines, power stations, factories, ports and airfields would also be possible targets. Unfortunately many people live near such 'legitimate' targets, and undoubtedly they would be at risk. If battlefield fighting seemed likely to take

place nearby as part of a nuclear theatre of tactical war, and if there were likely to be an extended conflict with both conventional and nuclear weapons involved, then ports and airfields could be high on the target priority list because these would be used to bring troops and munitions to the battlefield. In the end only you could decide whether you considered your area could be directly targeted with nuclear weapons and make your plans accordingly.

Obviously if everybody started to evacuate all danger areas there would be chaos. There would almost certainly be government restrictions: exit routes closed and guarded and petrol unavailable. And because you could not depend on getting more than a few minutes' warning of a nuclear attack, if you felt that evacuation was the best course you would have to be prepared to leave your home as soon as the international situation appeared dangerous – as we discuss in Chapter 7 that could be a very difficult decision – and before the use of nuclear weapons seemed inevitable.

If you did decide to evacuate you would need to be sure of two basic things: that you had adequate accommodation and fallout sheltering facilities in your new area and that you had a means of subsisting after an attack. Evacuation by itself might do no more than help you to stay alive for a few weeks or months. If you had not thought out your plans well ahead you could bring disaster upon yourself which might have been averted by staying at home. At the same time there would be little to recommend staying in a high-risk target area even if you had nowhere to go: if an attack did not take place you would at least live longer than if crushed by blast effects or burnt to a cinder.

Whatever you decided, you would have to keep clearly in mind that unless nuclear attack was of a very limited nature your long-term survival chances would be very slim in all events.

Where to go

Ideally you could emigrate to a country which is not in a possible war theatre (see pages 50–1), where it would be much less likely that nuclear warheads would be used. In reality there are few countries which could, or would, accept large numbers of immigrants. Third World countries are often overpopulated and have delicately balanced subsistence economies. Australia and New Zealand would seem logical choices, being advanced industrialized countries. But both have strict immigration laws. (Because many long-range missiles are based in the United States, Canada clearly cannot be regarded as 'safe'.) Clearly it is an illusion to imagine that by living in a non-combatant area you could escape totally the consequences of nuclear attack. As discussed in Chapter 4, among the most devastating effects of a nuclear war could be the economic consequences: the collapse of currencies and a return to barter as a means of conducting commerce and business, as well as the possibility of total loss of industrial production in countries attacked. Even so comparatively minor a catastrophe as the recent rises in oil prices has had widespread effects on the world community as a whole. The enormously greater consequences of a nuclear war could halt trade and development throughout the world, making it difficult to support indigenous populations let alone cope with the pressures of aiding any nuclear victims. So even evacuation from possible war theatres would not necessarily enable you to escape post-war difficulties.

A curious variety of attitudes towards civil defence planning exists in different countries, ranging from the concept of maximum personal protection provided in countries such as neutral Switzerland, Sweden, Finland Yugoslavia and similar places where it might justifiably be hoped that few warheads would be targeted, to the attitude of governments in countries such as Britain and America where minimal sums of public money are spent on civil defence. Britain abandoned its former policy of evacuation since it became clear that such action could not practically be made in the time scale which might be available before a nuclear attack, whereas the United States considers evacuation as a usable policy (perhaps because it might reasonably expect more warning of nuclear attack than any European country) which could reduce the casualties from a large scale attack from over 80 per cent of the population to less than 20 per cent under favourable circumstances. Despite impressive calculations, extensive discussions and various official publications about the benefits of such 'crisis relocation', however, America has not yet drawn up detailed plans even though this is one of the cheaper civil defence measures able to offer at least the hope of a significant reduction of civilian casualties.

The Soviet Union does not seem to share American reluctance to draw up evacuation plans, to design and build shelters and even prepare industrial plant for possible nuclear attack. Russia has indeed served as a 'fountain of ideas' for nuclear protection: many of the expedient shelter designs being studied in the United States have originated from the Soviet Union.

The Chinese also believe that civil defence is of great importance, taking shelter availability very seriously and have already carried out extensive building programmes. Although neither China nor the Soviet Union have constructed enough shelters or, as far as we know, have planned evacuation sufficiently well to offer the hope of a very large reduction of civilian casualties in the event of attack, the measures which have been taken would save some lives.

It is interesting to speculate why the same devotion to civil defence is not followed in the West. The answer may be that the democratic system of government necessarily submits any proposed civil defence expenditure to greater public scrutiny in the West. This would very probably lead to the whole concept of deterrence being severely questioned if a government stressed the need for any expensive programme of protective measures for the public. And of course it might encourage stronger criticism of military expenditure. Since Western governments hope and believe that deterrence will keep the peace, they are understandably reluctant to jeopardize their means to engage in it or to acknowledge that the policy might not be ideal by arguing for a big civil defence programme.

Sheltering

Shelters may be designed to protect against blast, heat and radiation or all three, but nobody should imagine that such protection would guarantee survival in the long term. Only very deep underground shelters could withstand a direct hit from a nuclear bomb. Shelters which many people could afford would only protect those lucky enough to be some distance from the point of explosion.

If you were away from a possible target's zone of severe blast and heat damage you would also be beyond the range of danger from initial radiation (unless low-yield weapons were used). Your main concern would be fallout radiation. In many plausible attack patterns, including the counter-force war (see pages 68–9), most survivors would be at risk mainly from fallout. So by preparing shelters which protect against fallout only, many lives could be saved in the short term.

Blast shelters

Shelters which protected against blast might keep people alive within the range where normal buildings were totally destroyed. For example, the Swiss government-approved shelters, made of thick, reinforced concrete, are designed to protect against blast (as well as heat and radiation). Even so these shelters would be vulnerable to a shortage of oxygen in the atmosphere outside if there were a fire storm. If you do not live in a possible target zone there would seem to be little point in building a blast-proof shelter. Because they need to be built of very expensive materials and be constructed under the supervision of a qualified engineer most people could not afford them in any case.

Fallout shelters

Many countries distribute official information on civil defence: numerous publications exist which advise the public how to protect themselves in the event of nuclear attack. Some of this official advice has come under a great deal of criticism. Illustrations showing families sheltering under tables and flights of stairs after all suggest that governments think that the public would believe that such modest precautions could protect against these most devastating weapons. But the official information concerns fallout, not blast effects, presumably because governments do not wish to spread alarm by detailing the consequences of blast and fire effects, about which very little could be done. However, these sources do contain useful information about fallout protection. The US Government, for example, has conducted extensive tests of various types of shelters which could be built by most people with no technical or craft knowledge. The tone of the resulting pamphlet, *Protection in the Nuclear Age*, unfortunately seems a little optimistic. Nevertheless the information is accurate, easy to understand and, if used in time, could save millions of lives in the short term if nuclear war actually took place. Similarly the official British pamphlet, *Protect and Survive*, contains useful, potentially life-saving information.

If you were not in a target area such official information guides might help. Many people would have to ignore the official government instructions to stay at home under all circumstances, however. As already discussed, this might be the best survival policy for many people, but in a high-risk target area it would clearly not be advisable.

Helping yourself

No matter how much any country develops civil defence shelters and procedures, protection from radiation cannot be guaranteed. Radiation protection would inevitably become an individual responsibility. No matter how good the intentions of your government might be, national leaders could have more pressing problems on their minds in wartime than the protection of civilians against radiation. Some help, such as fallout warnings, might be expected, but understanding the nature of radiation and its effects on the human body would be your best defence and could make it possible for you to do a great deal to help yourself.

Choosing a shelter

A fallout shelter should do two basic things:

1. It should prevent fallout dust particles from entering. If not, shelter occupants might inhale or swallow the dust, or it might stick to the skin or hair. Close contact with fallout would expose the victim to beta, and possible alpha, radiations which would otherwise not be a hazard (since both beta and alpha rays cannot penetrate even small thicknesses of material and certainly not walls and doors).

2. The shelter must be constructed of thick, solid, dense materials to absorb gamma radiation emitted by fallout and thus weaken the radiation hazard.

Shielding against radiation

The first rule, therefore, is that a shelter must be able to be sufficiently well sealed so that fallout dust could not enter. The remaining hazard would be the gamma radiation continually produced by the layer of fallout which would cover everything outside. The strength of this radiation would be greatly reduced by solid materials placed between the source of gamma rays and the people taking shelter. (This is why radiographers at hospitals use heavy lead screens as protection when working with x-rays.) All materials absorb gamma rays to some extent: in general, the heavier the material, the better the shielding. Lead is excellent as are other metals, especially heavy ones: iron is better than aluminium, for example. But many other common materials are also very efficient for radiation shielding purposes: house bricks, concrete and earth could all be used.

Fallout would settle everywhere so you would have to be shielded from every direction. If a shelter were at, or below, ground level, no radiation would penetrate it from below. But the walls and ceiling would have to be thick and heavy enough to absorb significant amounts of gamma radiation. The radiation-absorbing quality of any material depends mainly on its density. (If, for example, you had 100 pounds of material on every square foot of a wall or ceiling, this

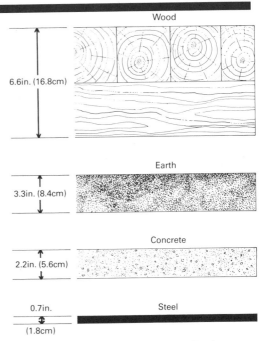

Different thicknesses of material can give the same degree of protection against gamma rays. Thus 6.6 inches (16.8 cm) of wood gives the same protection as 0.7 inches (1.8 cm) of steel.

would produce almost exactly the same shielding from gamma radiation whatever material was used.)

Clearly a shield made from wood has to be a great deal thicker than one made from concrete, which in turn must be much thicker than a shield made from lead capable of absorbing gamma radiation to the same extent.

Half-value thickness

A measurement which expresses the ability of a substance to absorb gamma radiation from fallout is called the 'half-value thickness': that is, the thickness of the material required to reduce the intensity of a beam of gamma radiation to one half of its strength. Concrete, for example, has a half-value thickness of approximately 2.2 inches (5.6 cm).

Even 20 miles away from a nuclear explosion, the fallout dose rate outside could reach 1,000 r per hour or more for anybody exposed outside. If you were inside a shelter made of concrete 2.2 inches thick, however,

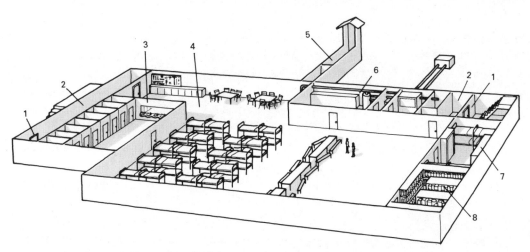

Because the Soviet Union and the United States possess nuclear weapons their approach to civil defence is subtly different from that of a country like Sweden which is neutral and has no nuclear arms. Both the superpowers have numbers of public shelters in major cities. Signs indicating their whereabouts are a familiar sight to New Yorkers, for example. New underground railway stations in Moscow have incorporated features which would facilitate fallout protection in the event of nuclear attack. However, although the plan of a Russian public basement shelter (**above**), for instance,

(blast door (1); air lock (2); toilet facilities (3); accommodation area (4); emergency tunnel and exit (5); filter units (6); medical room (7), and food preparation and store room (8)) has many similarities with the segment of a Swedish underground control centre (**centre opposite**) such shelters would probably never be built in large numbers to give most Soviet citizens protection.

On the other hand every Swedish citizen can be assured of the maximum amount of publicly-funded protection which could be politically justified.

The above-ground Swedish shelter (**left**) is used as a school in peacetime. But if hostilities broke out it could immediately be utilised as a shelter. Stockholm's main control point (**right**) is built in a rock cavern and has its entrance (8) near the city centre. It consists of three main buildings: the administrative centre (3), the accommodation building (4) and the power plant (6). The two emergency exits (1, 7) complete with shock wave barriers (2) are used to supply and expel air to and from the shelter. Filters (5) purify the air supplied to the main buildings.

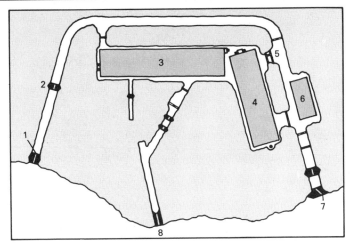

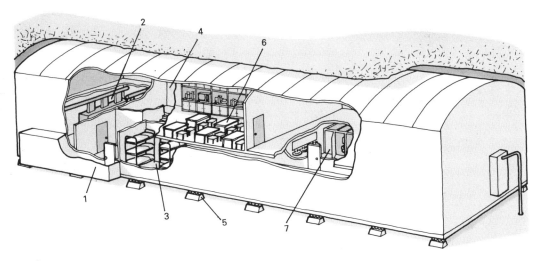

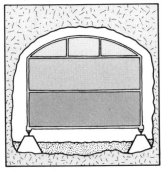

The two-storey control centre is mounted on springs (see cross-section (**left**)) which reduce the effects of ground shock waves. To eliminate the effects of electromagnetic pulses produced by a nuclear explosion, which burn out electronic circuits, the buildings are clad in steel sheeting. The administrative building which contains communications facilities, medical care rooms, kitchen and dining room, control rooms and the stores for the centre is connected to the accommodation block (**above**). Apart from the sleeping areas (3) it also contains a workroom (6), toilet facilities (7) and, like all the buildings in the complex, its own air filter equipment (2) and emergency exits (1, 4). Properly engineered structures like this one, with its shock-resistent foundations (5) and an adequate cover for fallout protection are justified in countries like Switzerland and Sweden. But if the superpowers built such extensive underground facilities there is a danger that these would simply be attacked with bigger bombs: there would be no escape from the holocaust.

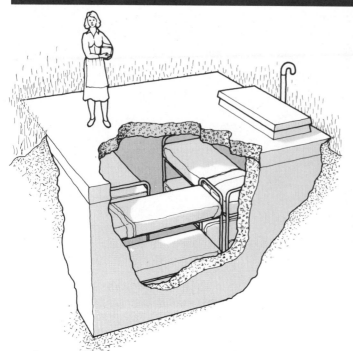

Left The American, British and French Governments do not provide the public with home shelters. An underground shelter at home, built in the garden, would cost a great deal and would give no certainty of survival in the event of all-out nuclear war. Such shelters would be better than basement shelters because masonry and brickwork would be less likely to trap the occupants inside. Most shelters of this type would be the recommended minimum size (about that of a bathroom) for reasons of cost and would be claustrophobic even under the best conditions. Under nuclear attack, life inside one would be terrifying. Many shelter-owners might die in their house or at work, being unable to reach the shelter before the arrival of the warheads.

Below Humidity, damp, stench and overheating would add to the terror of shelter life. Although ventilation units like this Swiss one could improve conditions, few citizens in nuclear-armed countries are likely to get them.

this dose rate would be reduced by half to 500 rph. This would still give you a lethal dose within one hour (the LD 50 dose equals approximately 450 r, see page 43). But a shelter made of concrete 4.4 inches thick (two half-value thicknesses) would reduce the dose rate to 250 rph, 6.6 inches of concrete halves the dose rate again bringing it down to 125 rph. It is clear that by sheltering within a concrete shield several feet thick even a very strong rate of gamma emission from fallout radiation outside the shelter would be reduced to a mere trickle within.

From the half-value thicknesses of various building materials it is possible to calculate the amount of protection any shelter would give. Any building would give some protection because the bricks, glass, tiles and other materials it is made of are all capable of absorbing gamma radiation to some extent. Although the amount of shielding depends on many factors (such as the exact thickness of walls) it is possible to say approximately how much fallout protection different kinds of buildings would give on average. This is known as the protective factor (PF) of a particular build-

Right Commercial companies are cashing in on the 'doom boom' with countless shelter designs, some of them safe and liable to give good blast or fallout protection, others of more dubious quality. A cylindrical corrugated shelter (**above**) to protect against fallout which needs to be covered with dirt in the garden has been built to British Home Office recommendations and is equipped with an air filter unit worked by the shelter occupants.

ing. A PF of ten, for example, implies that anybody who was sheltering in a building having this protective factor would receive a radiation dose reduced by a factor of ten, compared with an unprotected person outside. If the building or shelter had a PF of 100, then a highly dangerous external dose rate of 100 rph would be reduced to a more tolerable rate of only one rph inside the shelter.

In the case of an accumulated dose of 900 r after one week (in a 1-Mt attack on a single city, page 63), anybody sheltering within a building having a PF of ten would receive the reduced dose of 90 r, which would cause no immediate ill effects.

The Soviet Union has designed a wide range of shelters, among them prefabricated constructions made from pipe or duct sections. Besides the sanitation (1) and accommodation (2) area, each of these cleverly-planned shelters has an air filter (4) containing sand or slag, with a pump powered by hand (3) or legs (note the bicycle (5)). Impressive as these shelters seem not enough are available. They do nevertheless slightly improve the USSR's ability to 'survive' nuclear attack, but more importantly they improve public confidence in the Government.

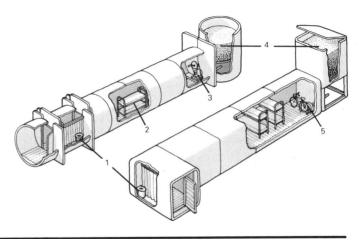

A basement shelter protects against fallout unless dust gets in through the broken windows and roof of the house. Fire and blast damage to the house could still be lethal.

All daylight would have to be excluded and ventilation would be difficult.

Approximate protective factors for various buildings

Structure	P.F.
three feet underground	5,000
frame house	1.5–3.0
basement	10–20
multistory building (apartment type)	
upper stories	100
lower stories	10
concrete blockhouse shelter	
9-inch walls	10–150
12-inch walls	30–1,000
24-inch walls	500–10,000
Shelter, partly above ground	
with two-foot earth cover	50–200
with three-foot earth cover	200–1,000

Source: *The Effect of Nuclear Weapons* by Glasstone and Dolan, 3rd Edition, U.S. Department of Defense and U.S. Department of Energy, 1977, p. 441.

How much shielding is necessary?

Maximum dose rates greater than 5,000 r per hour are predicted to be unlikely from fallout except perhaps in small isolated 'hot spots' (where rain, snow or wind might have concentrated the fallout), or very close to ground zero. The *total* dose, taking into account the fact that the dose *rate* would fall off quickly with time, in the worst case would be about 15,000 r, most of which would be emitted within a few weeks. (Total dose in any place is *very approximately* three times the maximum dose per hour shortly after the explosion.[1])

A building with a PF of 100 would reduce this to 150 r, which is the highest dose the average person could receive without developing radiation sickness. As you can see from the table opposite, most buildings have PFs lower than 100, so at the worst possible location in the fallout distribution people in buildings would develop radiation sickness and many would die.

But as it is unlikely that most places

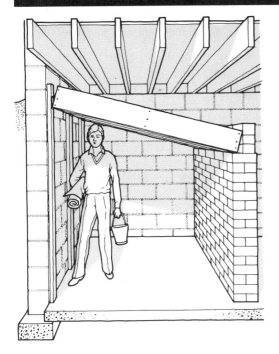

Do-it-yourself hobbyists might devise ways of increasing the overhead thickness of fallout shielding in a basement shelter: a futile gesture if rainwater washed fallout inside.

The 'lean-to' radiation shield inside the basement shelter genuinely improves a person's chances of avoiding radiation sickness.

would be subjected to this worst possible dose of fallout radiation, clearly ordinary buildings, provided they remained standing, could give sufficient shielding in many places. A more likely total accumulated dose of 1,500 r (even in the areas of highest fallout concentration) would be reduced to 150 r by a building having a PF of only ten. Thus even some single-storey houses might

provide enough protection to save lives.

If you wanted a PF of 1,000, for example (which would confer very significant protection even in the worst affected fallout areas), this could be achieved by building the shelter walls and roof with concrete 22 inches (56cm) thick. This 22 inches comes from ten half-value thicknesses of concrete (each one 2.2 inches), be-

The well-prepared basement shelterer would have piled up dirt around the exterior walls of the house and on the floor of the ground floor over the basement. A hand-operated pump would draw air through a filter to refresh the putrid air, and extra beams within the basement would strengthen the roof. But how many people would do all this?

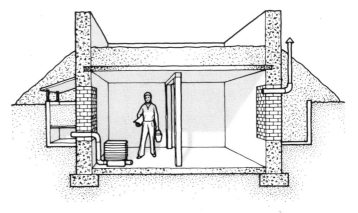

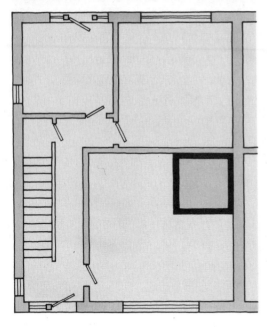

With extra shielding the innermost corner of the innermost room would give best fallout protection provided the dust didn't enter a broken window.

cause this would reduce the intensity of radiation by a factor of just over 1,000 ($2^{10} = 2\times2\times2\times2\times2\times2\times2\times2\times2\times2 = 1024$).

In practice you would not need as much concrete on the walls as you would have to incorporate in a flat roof, because hardly any fallout would stick to the walls whereas a roof would form an easy resting place for the dust. It is interesting to note that the Swiss make use of a minimum thickness of 22 inches of concrete for ceilings which have no other shielding material (such as soil) on top. (In the Swiss designs the walls are thicker – 32 inches (80cm) – to withstand greater blast forces: the shelters are designed to protect against blast as well as fallout.) From the calculations shown above it appears that the Swiss shelters would give PFs of at least 1,000, capable of reducing even the worst conceivable accumulated dose of 15,000 r to a mere 15 r, a dose which could be harmless.

The same protection would be conferred by 33 inches (84cm) of earth (also ten half-value thicknesses) although the density, and therefore the half-value thicknesses, can vary slightly. Nevertheless, it can be said that a shielding of earth approximately 3 feet (1 metre) thick would give a PF of at least 1,000 and any type of shelter which is buried that far underground would give very good fallout protection. Obviously it would be easiest to achieve such a high PF by digging a shelter into the ground: you would then automatically have *very* thick walls, and the only point of entry for the fallout radiation would be through the roof of the shelter.

Staying inside a building

Radiation can shine into a building through the walls and windows as well as the roof. In theory it is certainly possible to increase the building's PF by making some modifications.

Piling earth against the outer walls up to the first storey is a recommended modification. This would be particularly important in buildings without basements. If the building had a basement this could be used as the basic fallout shelter. If not, an inner room as far away from external walls and roof as possible would be chosen. The walls or places giving the *least* radiation shielding would have to be blocked up with bricks or have furniture placed in front of them. Because glass is very thin and shatters easily windows give almost no protection. All the windows in the building could be covered with adhesive tape to reduce the amount of shattered glass caused by the blast pressure from the explosion and painted with white paint to deflect the heat from the flash and so prevent fires.

The walls and ceiling of the room or basement could be reinforced with extra shielding materials. Part of the room should be sectioned off and shielded with extra protective materials. This is where the question of 'hiding under the table' comes in. Although it seems laughably inadequate, if your house were not blasted down or had not caught fire, you could get extra protection from radioactive fallout by crawling under a table covered with every heavy object you could find. This is where you would be advised to spend most of your time when the fallout was at its most intense. This could vary from a few days to weeks if there were a number of attacks.

So you would have to block up the windows of the room where you wanted to shelter, paint and tape or paper over all other windows in the house, reinforce your shelter with shielding materials and build a place within the shelter room with extra radiation protection. You could well live long enough to have to cope with the many other dire consequences of nuclear attack.

You should not get over-enthusiastic about these various protective features mentioned however. They would take, at the least, several hours to execute properly and, because it is doubtful that anyone would go to the lengths described unless they knew for certain there was going to be a nuclear attack, it seems unlikely that there would be time to make these preparations. You would, of course, need to assemble essential food and water supplies as well. And the effects of a nuclear attack would be so severe that you need to comprehend the full range of consequences and the likely impact they would have on society as a whole.

Hiding under the stairs may sound ridiculous but it could give protection against radiation if the house remained standing.

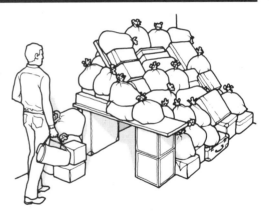

An 'inner refuge' would be necessary because few houses would give enough fallout protection even with the windows intact.

Effects on radio and radar signals
Nuclear explosions cause ionisation (electrification) of large numbers of air molecules. This can degrade some radio and radar signals, giving poor reception, and cause a complete blackout especially of short-wave (high frequency) signals.

Most local radio broadcasts using medium frequency or VHF (very high frequency) would hardly be affected. Neither would television signals which use both VHF and UHF (ultra high frequency). But short-wave broadcasts could be blacked out for minutes or hours because of disruption to the earth's ionised upper atmosphere.

Electromagnetic pulse
The nuclear fireball could act like a gigantic radio transmitter generating radio signals on all frequencies simultaneously in one powerful pulse. Such a pulse of energy could generate large electric voltages and currents in electrical conductors (such as telephone lines and radio aerials) within a radius of several miles. Solid state electronic circuits in radios, computers, calculators, telephone equipment, watches and many other devices could be burnt out by the pulse. It would not harm humans.

'Expedient' shelters

'Expedient' shelters could protect against fallout (some are also blast resistent) and can be made within 48 hours by unskilled people, entirely from local materials (although huge sheets of polythene plastic are an advantage for building most of these).

We include some of the more straightforward expedient shelter designs listed in *The Expedient Shelter Handbook*, published by Oak Ridge National Laboratory, Tennessee.

Imagine what life would be like, cooped up for weeks on end within such structures, and you will have some idea of shelter conditions after an attack. Add to this the fear of further attack, grief for lost relatives, lack of food, petrol, your home and practically everything we normally require for happiness and comfort. Sheltering would be desperate, terrifying and for many people the last few weeks of life: because among the millions taking shelter after an attack, most would be likely to die in the weeks and months which follow unless the attack was of a very limited nature indeed.

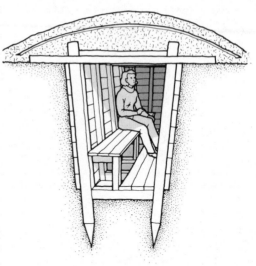

Above This trench expedient shelter might be enjoyable to build given the necessary 48 hours warning of attack. The dank, sordid, cramped conditions, however, might be intolerable after a few days.

Below Sophisticated trench expedient shelters could be built by groups co-operating and would give protection. In practice the terror of impending nuclear attack might wreck the best of intentions and sheltering plans.

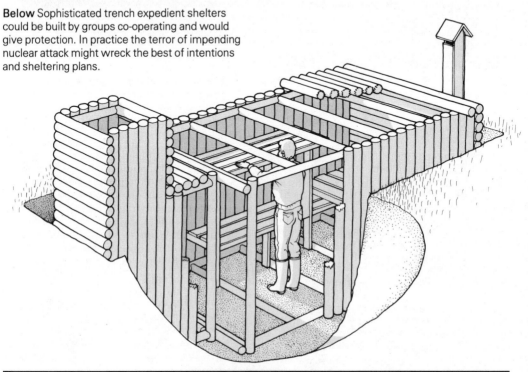

Caravan/trailer-in-trench shelter

Car-over-trench shelter

Doors-over-trench shelter

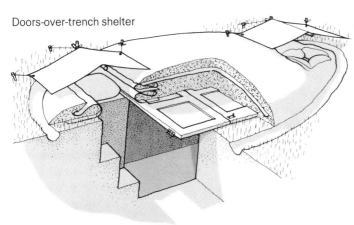

Expedient shelters are an appealing concept because nothing has to be prepared, other than shelter designs, until war becomes imminent. For a high standard of shelter living the trailer or vehicle driven into a wide trench and covered with dirt (**top**) offers good protection from fallout. The car-over-trench expedient shelter (**centre**) is designed for people who intend to drive away from target areas (equipped with spades and other tools necessary to prepare the shelter). The simplest type is the door-over-trench shelter (**bottom**) which is protected from rain by sheets of polythene or other non-porous material. Earth provides the radiation shielding. Expedient shelters are designed to make use of available materials and should not take more than 48 hours to build. They are proposed because of the proven wisdom of evacuation to limit immediate casualties. But such shelters are obviously useless if no warning of attack is given. It is also doubtful whether under the most optimistic conditions frightened city dwellers would successfully build the structures in time to save themselves from fallout.

6 If you wish to prepare

Whether we like it or not we live continuously with a small but finite risk that nuclear war will actually happen. This can only change if the world finds some other policy to replace nuclear deterrence. Until that happens it is very understandable to want to make some preparations for survival, even though only a few people might find themselves in a position to take advantage of any knowledge they had acquired or preparations they may have made.

Preparations would have to be both short and long term, and they might have to be adapted at short notice. If you survived the attack but were seriously injured or suffering from radiation sickness your continued survival would depend largely on others. If you survived you might have other people depending on you, especially if you were close to the areas of devastation. In this case short-term survival planning could be crucial in keeping you and your dependents alive long enough to benefit from any long-term measures, whether these depended on others or were measures you had planned yourself.

Alternatively you might find yourself, by chance, far away from the attack zone. In this case your main concern would be surviving in the long term, but would probably prove to be almost as formidable because there would be many other survivors, injured or healthy, who at some time would need help from you.

The end of hostilities?
Probably the biggest uncertainty would be knowing whether the attack had ended or not. You might have no way of telling whether a limited initial bombardment had succeeded in 'winning' a war or was the signal that many more nuclear warheads were about to be detonated in areas so far unscathed. Because most of the actions necessary for self preservation would be dangerous if the conflict continued you might die because of lack of information.

You would only know definitely that war was at an end if you received news that the Government had negotiated peace or that there had been a successful invasion of enemy troops. Obviously, an undamaged portable radio would be a great help, particularly if it could receive short-wave transmissions which, although they might not reach you for many hours after an attack (because of temporary changes in the ionosphere caused by nuclear explosions), would almost certainly provide you with news after a day or so. Even after a large-scale attack local radio stations might be able to begin broadcasts in some parts of the country a few days later and those situated in remote parts of the country might not have ceased transmissions at all.

The uncertainties of surviving
The psychological effect of an attack would be severe, even among physically healthy survivors. Even those who had become 'experts' on the subject by study and wide reading would find the actual warfare terrifying, and with just cause: even limited attacks would cause death and destruction beyond the imagination of most people. Bereavement, the lack of all normal com-

munications and services we normally take for granted, such as electricity, gas, water, transport and shops, might shatter the confidence and optimism of even the most stout-hearted.

Imagine yourself surviving with, for example, a lost child, a dead or dying spouse, your face lacerated with a hundred glass fragments and your doctor dead or out of reach, and you will begin to appreciate some of the problems you could encounter. Add to this the sordid conditions of life within an improvised fallout shelter or modified building from which daylight was excluded (because of the necessary fallout shielding) and normal sanitary facilities were lacking and you will realise that survival would be far from easy. By facing such possibilities in advance, however, you might at least be able to prevent yourself from going mad if it all happened.

Although it is wise to make survival plans, it is foolish to imagine they could make nuclear war truly survivable. Whatever happened some people would survive, but the post-attack world would almost certainly be drastically changed.

Survival plans are necessary for another reason, however. Although many people think they would rather die than face the horrors of post-attack living, if an attack really took place these same people might find that many other survivors would depend on them: relatives and friends might need help. If half of your compatriots were dead and many of the survivors injured how could you reasonably expect to get help from outside? It is a myth to expect that any government would have any significant ability to cope with the crisis of a really massive attack. So there might be no *official* help, but there could be *community* help, from people in very similar predicaments to your own. After an attack you would need to offer your assistance every bit as much as to receive assistance. Without community cohesion and cooperation, survival would be even less likely. Faced with the grim reality that nuclear war might happen, everybody has a duty to co-operate and work for the future however uncertain this might be.

It is sometimes observed that the quality

of post-attack life among survivors would be better if the majority of the population died from short-term bomb effects: the greater the number of people who survive the early stages of attack, the more massive and possibly brutal might be the scramble for diminishing stocks of food and water later on. But all such discussions are hypothetical in the extreme because one of the main findings of studies about the effects of nuclear war is that everything is uncertain except that massive destruction and slaughter could take place. Individuals can only make the best preparations they can in the hope that things might take a turn for the better.

Stocking up for survival

It goes almost without saying that food and water are among the most important priorities both for short- and long-term survival. A water supply would be the most pressing need immediately after an attack, and obtaining uncontaminated water (free from fallout) would become very difficult if the attack were extended. There might be plenty of food in the country (depending on the season in which the attack took place: just before harvest would prevent the reaping of crops and cause a food shortage during the winter) but the normal methods of distribution, by road and rail, would almost certainly be lacking. In all events your own food and water stocks would help, and the larger the stocks the better your chance of surviving during the following months.

In building up stocks of food and water you would have to bear in mind that given enough warning time of an attack the best response for many people would be to evacuate. Towns and cities are necessarily close to industrial buildings and factories which might not be spared attack if the final 'rung' of the war escalation ladder were reached. By spreading the population over the country it is a fact that fewer people would suffer from immediate bomb effects. American studies[1] suggest that immediate casualties from a large attack might be reduced in the United States by a timely evacuation to about 20 per cent. In practice however

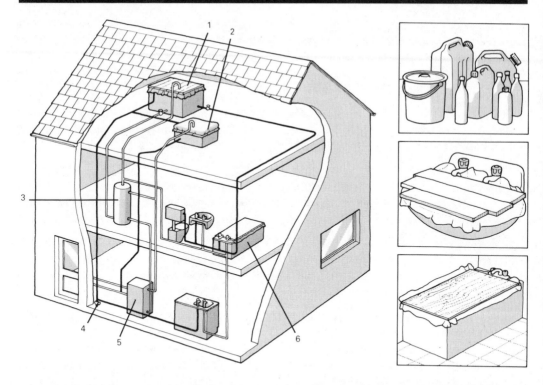

If the mains tap (4) were turned off, water trapped in a cold water tank (1), central heating header tank (2), hot water tank (3), bath (6), boiler (5), and the pipe-work would be uncontaminated and could keep a family alive if carefully stored (insets).

organised evacuation might not take place. But this need not prevent individuals from evacuating independently of government plans. Not all countries could benefit as much as the United States from evacuating, and calculations comparable with American ones are not readily available for most other countries, but short-term casualties could certainly be reduced anywhere. By evacuating you might run into insurmountable problems after a few weeks. But you would at least have a better chance of being alive as long as this. Because of the possible need for evacuation your food and water stocks would have to be portable, or you would need to have a remote hideaway ready and stocked for occupation.

You might, however, adopt a more fatalistic approach: acknowledging that the decision of when to evacuate as well as where

to, would be an almost impossible one to make, you might stock up your home and simply hope it remained standing after the attack.

Essential water supplies

If you wished to improve your survival chances *very slightly* you would need to begin preparations well in advance of the attack and stockpile water, using every container at your disposal: plastic buckets, bottles, tanks and the like. You might decide to put sealed containers full of water in plastic sacks and bury them in the garden as an emergency supply in case your house fell down but you were able to crawl out of the ruins. Water is essential to life, indeed it is the basic ingredient of every cell of our bodies. Adults can live without food for several weeks, but even a day without water can be fatal in hot dry conditions.

Immediately after an attack your domestic water supply would be unlikely to be working normally even if your house were undamaged. Mains water supplies which were still working might be contaminated with fallout, so you would be reluctant to use them anyway (though to risk a slow death from radiation sickness might be better than an assured and speedy end from thirst). If your house remained standing you might be able to use clean water trapped in the plumbing system. Central heating units, hot water systems and lavatories all usually have their own 'header tanks' to supply the appropriate water pressure. If you were able to turn off the mains water supply to prevent contaminated water entering the system you might then be able to drain the clean water from these tanks and keep a group alive for several weeks. If you followed government instructions (such as those in the British pamphlet *Protect and Survive*) you would have filled the bath, sinks, buckets and all other nearby containers at first warning of the attack. You might have had to use some of this water to put out fires however.

Depending on your location at the time of the attack you might look for likely places for digging a well. Ground water could be contaminated with microbes and chemicals, but there might be a good chance that it would be free from fallout which (with the exception of radio-iodine) is mostly insoluble in water. So a well might form an adequate water source after an attack. (It must be emphasised that all of these measures would be desperate ones. Most factors influencing your survival would be out of your control, but this might not deter you

The 'quartz fiber pocket electrometer' is one of a range of instruments which could give warning of excessive radiation exposure. But very few people outside the nuclear industry possess such devices.

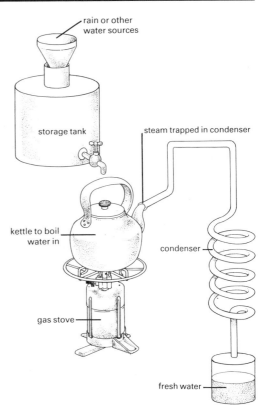

Distillation is the most effective method of purifying water. In most countries, however, it is difficult to buy good stills because of governments' desire to collect alcohol duties.

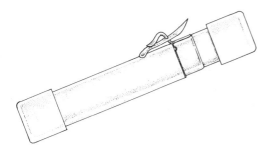

from doing everything possible, even if this amounted in practice to 'grasping at straws'.)

You would have to be able to clean and purify the water and decontaminate it from fallout. An instrument for measuring radiation (such as a Geiger Counter) would make fallout detection possible, otherwise you would have to treat all types of dust and dirt as suspect. (If an attack seemed imminent, however, the demand for Geiger Counters would certainly exceed supplies.) To clean rainwater or water from a ditch, culvert or muddy stream you would have to leave it to settle in a bucket or tank for about 24 hours. Most of the solids (including fallout) would then form a sediment at the bottom and you would be able to draw relatively clean water from the top. Having done this you could also filter (through a coffee filter or a fabric such as a towel or handkerchief) and boil it (if you had a stove). It would be enormously helpful to have some 'water purifying tablets' used by camping enthusiasts and available from pharmacists which kill microorganisms. They ensure that anybody drinking the water (who might have diminished natural disease fighting mechanisms because of exposure to radiation) would not get infected from it. If you did not have such tablets, you could add a few drops of household bleach to each pint of water (checking that it contains only 'hypochlorite' and not some toxic ingredient), or several drops of tincture of iodine solution.

Storing food

You would need to store adequate stocks of food. Although some countries might have perhaps a year's supply of farm crops in storage it might not be possible to get any of it. If a large scale attack were successful government might be emasculated. Even if strong government survived, the loss of oil refineries (among the most likely of economic targets) would ensure that gasoline and diesel oil would not be easily available for transportation. So in order to give yourself any reasonable degree of long-term protection you would need a year's personal supply of food. And having stocked up with adequate supplies for your own use you would be faced with the moral dilemma after an attack of whether to share your stocks with others who did not have your foresight.

Presuming that you did decide to store food what items would you need? Freezers and refrigerators would not work, indeed you might have to say goodbye to mains electricity and gas for a long time as even the 'optimists' suggest that there could be a return to an eighteenth-century standard of living after a large attack. So you would have to choose canned food, and dried grains, cereals and vegetables, together with foods preserved by salting, pickling, smoking and so on. You might decide to keep a good stock of canned meat for two reasons: firstly it would be a scarce luxury after an attack (it would be extremely expensive to build adequate fallout shelters for farm animals, so few would survive an attack in which counterforce targets are included using surface-burst weapons), but secondly it might become a form of currency in the barter economy which could grow up after an attack to replace coins and notes. The same might be said of alcohol and tobacco, though these products do not themselves confer any survival advantage.

Most official information on the subject of stocking up for survival after a nuclear attack discusses a limited 'shelter period', usually of two weeks, during which citizens would have to stay within fallout shelters or risk radiation sickness by going outside. Food stocks suggested are usually sufficient for this period. (In fact the two weeks is carefully chosen, being the length of time necessary for fallout radiation to diminish in strength even in severely contaminated places sufficiently to allow many normal outdoor activities.) These pamphlets, however, assume that the Government would be in a position to tell you what to do after the shelter period. This might not happen in practice, so if you only stock enough food for two weeks you might die soon thereafter. Another fault in the two week shelter period theory is that those sheltering would not easily be able to make certain that war had ended. They would probably fear to come out of the shelters after a fortnight. To do so would probably involve facing unknown hazards, even if the claustrophobic and unsanitary shelter conditions themselves were dangerous.

Living conditions in a shelter

It would prove difficult, messy and unhygienic to prepare meals in a shelter and dispose of the scraps. The most primitive improvised fallout shelters, such as a trench in the open covered with dirt, would certainly become intolerable after a few days. You might have to leave the shelter and take the risk of fallout rather than stay squashed like sardines (taking official 'expedient shelter' plans) having less space than two people in a shower cubicle would, or the equivalent of having ten people crowded into the space (but not the shape) of the average bathroom.

One of the worst aspects of shelter life would be the stench of the makeshift bucket latrine. Diarrhoea and vomit from radiation sickness would increase the misery.

If you succeeded in providing your group with a more 'luxurious' shelter, such as a basement or a ground-floor room you would nevertheless find conditions sordid and frightening. You could, for example, have your mother's dead body in the room (she might have been burnt or injured severely or have been exposed to radiation or any combination of these). You might have to explain what had happened to her to your small children. You would have to prepare your (mainly cold) meals while (if the weather were hot) flies swarmed over the corpse and around the makeshift latrine (a bucket with a plastic 'liner' bag inside) standing in one corner of the room. You could have a broken arm and might wonder whether your children had been exposed to harmful doses of radiation. The symptoms of sheer panic are remarkably similar to those of radiation sickness, and knowing that it can take weeks or months for a victim to die from radiation sickness you might be wondering how many of your family might ultimately survive. It would be a terrifying, sickening experience.

It has to be emphasised that only a minority of people would find themselves in this situation, however. These conditions would apply only to people who had sur-vived on the fringes of areas of devastation or who were caught in the path of a fallout plume. After a small attack many would survive without having to stay in shelters, and those living in areas contaminated by fallout might be able to move away swiftly without being badly exposed to radiation. In a large attack the majority would die, and there might be more (but still not many) survivors in remote areas (saved from fall-out by favourable winds blowing the dust away from them) than people sheltering in fringe-areas. In studying how to shelter successfully you must accept that the possible protective measures could only *marginally* improve your overall survival chances.

You would spend most of your time during the shelter period in near-darkness or dim lighting because there would be no mains electricity, and supplies of candles and torch batteries would be limited so you would want to conserve them as much as possible. The same would apply to canisters of gas, such as those used for camping which, if you had a stove, would enable you to prepare some hot meals. You would probably decide to use these sparingly, not knowing when it might be safe to emerge.

A camping stove would provide some hot meals during fallout sheltering, at the expense of burning up oxygen and increasing the humidity of the shelter air.

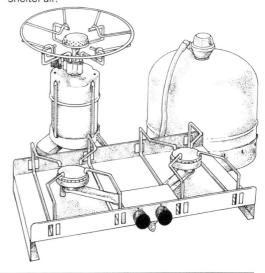

Cooking could be limited to boiling eggs and then using the hot water to make tea or coffee. It would be over-optimistic to expect much more than this: most meals would have to be cold because cooking would not only be prohibited by the need to conserve fuel supplies but could also cause ventilation problems.

In an enclosed shelter the air would get foul and humid and cooking would add to this. To reduce the humidity it would be essential to ventilate the shelter, but in the simplest shelters (or those most hastily improvised) to do so might invite the entry of fallout dust. If you were able to construct your refuge in a basement or in an inner room of a building, you would have to leave an interior door open. Even then the ventilation might not be enough, and you might have to venture out of the 'sanctuary' to open outer doors or windows, or stand at the door of your shelter and fan the air to make a draught.

Coping with sickness

Nothing would be easy. Everything would be fraught with dangers, uncertainty and terror. Many people in the shelters would have to face up to the realisation that they were slowly dying from injuries or radiation sickness. They could expect no medical help because the sheer magnitude of the crisis would overwhelm organised emergency services. Your shelter could become your coffin.

Knowledge of medicine and first aid techniques, together with a suitable stock of bandages, ointments, simple drugs and other medicines might help you. Again it has to be emphasised that we are talking about a *small* improvement in your survival chances, and even then only if you were lucky enough to be among the group of survivors who by accident were able to use such skills to help themselves.

You could put together a big first aid kit. Bandages, gauze and other dry dressings would be among the most useful items, together with sticking plaster: anything to help keep wounds clean in the filthy living conditions of a fallout shelter. Burns and lacerations (from flying glass) might be the most common injuries. You would not be

able to do much to treat a burn, other than to keep dirt away and give the patient fluids (including salt water) to help prevent shock. Your bandages and sticking plaster could help skin lacerations to heal, though you would have to try to extract any pieces of glass from the wounds. Glass fragments propelled by the blast pressure could easily penetrate a quarter of an inch or so into human flesh, so you might find yourself spending hours by candlelight manipulating the flesh of your child's bloody face like a piece of meat in an attempt to extract the pieces of glass. If you had one injury to deal with, however, you would almost certainly have others: so after dealing with lacerations to one person you might have to stretch someone else's broken shin bone to set it in position ready for splinting. While you were performing these tasks you could start to vomit and feel feverish. This might indicate the first signs of radiation sickness, or it could simply be a reaction to the horrors of your experiences. If the vomiting stopped you might then have a few days without symptoms during which you would wonder whether diarrhoea was going to begin. If it did, and if again you began to develop feverish symptoms you would have your fears of radiation sickness confirmed. Others in the shelter might also be suffering from radiation sickness, and not knowing what doses each had received (unless you carried radiation dosimeters) you would have little idea whether the disease would be fatal or not. Needless to say, claustrophobic shelter life would be made no better by having most shelter occupants suffering from diarrhoea and vomiting.

Your first aid kit would have to include strong disinfectants and deodorants which could be used to kill germs as well as reducing the stench of sickness which might otherwise overpower the shelter. The unhygienic conditions could easily lead to a rapid spread of infections. This could be made far worse if shelterers had been exposed to radiation because natural defences against disease can be severely weakened by radiation. If you had persuaded your doctor before the attack to prescribe a variety of antibiotic drugs to fight bacterial infections you might be able to use them to prevent burns from getting infected and to halt infections resulting from internal bleeding and external wounds.

Potassium iodine could be included in your medical supplies. This provides a large amount of iodine to the thyroid gland and thus protects it from the radioisotope iodine present in fallout which seeks the gland on entering the body. The principle of thyroid protection is that by 'filling up' the gland with safe iodine it is not likely to absorb radio-iodine so easily. By giving this to children you might hope to prevent them from suffering growth disturbances which might otherwise result from an accumulation of the radioisotope in the thyroid.

The care of infants would add to the problems of shelter life. Babies would be far better off if breast fed, though almost every aspect of infant care would be difficult in a shelter. The baby might cry inconsolably and because of being less resistent to infections, extremes of temperature and humidity and radiation might die.

It is very hard to see how shelter living could possibly be anything other than miserable, filthy, terrifying, demoralising and devoid of almost everything we normally expect from life. It would not even offer a good chance of survival, because it is appropriate only for those people in the fringe areas and as these are (by definition) located between the areas of devastation and the unscathed parts of the country, they would inevitably include many people with injuries.

The fallout hazard

Military aims are not fulfilled primarily by murdering civilians, terrifying them or intentionally exposing them to fallout. To make nuclear war-fighting more 'thinkable' and 'acceptable' military commanders would almost certainly 'air burst' weapons wherever possible to avoid fallout. If people in the attacked region could be informed that this was the case it might be possible for those who had escaped death from the blast and heat to dispense with the hardship of a shelter period. The trouble is that nobody has devised an effective means of

informing survivors whether the weapons are air-burst or not. Individuals might prefer to stay under shelter anyway for fear of further bombardment: there is at least psychological protection in a shelter even if a fallout shelter does not protect against blast.

The fear of fallout could of course be used as a potent weapon just as much as (probably more than) fallout itself. A single nuclear detonation could send everybody running to the fallout shelters. This might cause enough disruption to win a war. So if you were installed in a shelter you would need to ask yourself whether your best interests were being served by staying there. Without telephone, radio or TV and without a Geiger Counter you might only be able to guess.

If you decided that it was imperative to stay in some sort of fallout shelter you would ultimately have the problem of how to cope with the fallout dust lying on and around the shelter. Some of it might get into your shelter through a door or window. At the end of the shelter period (say two weeks after the last explosion) you might have to leave the shelter to look for water, food and help. Even before that period you might have to drag any decaying corpses outside and you might have to leave the shelter briefly to throw out plastic bags of toilet refuse in order to reduce the stench within the shelter. All of these operations would involve the risk of exposure to radiation, though how great the risk might be would be impossible to tell unless you had a radiation-measuring instrument. Young children should not do these tasks, neither should pregnant women nor anyone who wishes to have children because it is the young and the unborn who are at the greatest risk from radiation.

The person leaving the shelter would, ideally, be completely covered from head to foot (goggles could be worn to protect the eyes) to prevent fallout getting on the skin and hair, and would have to 'decontaminate' on returning to the shelter. Fallout consists of dust, sometimes easily visible (including large flakes in places close to the explosion) but sometimes so fine as to remain invisible.

It would have to be assumed that you had been covered with fallout, so you would have to remove all clothes and wash as thoroughly as possible. You would have to leave any clothes, shoes and equipment outside the shelter together with towels used for drying after washing. The ideal 'decontamination area' (in a purpose built shelter) would be an ante-room with a shower and a draft of air gently blowing through from inside the shelter to the outside. Such facilities are included in many of the sophisticated shelters such as those constructed in Switzerland. Nothing, however, can make decontamination easy or completely reliable. It might be necessary, for example, to shave off your hair if you could not get the dust out of it. And if you were unfortunate enough to swallow fallout dust or inhale it decontamination would be almost impossible except, perhaps, by drastic medical procedures, and even then with no guarantee of success.

Decontaminating food would be another problem. You might not be able to store enough food inside your fallout shelter and the stocks left outside might get covered with fallout dust. Cans of food could be washed in water and the contents would then be completely safe to eat. Anything sealed in plastic bags or waterproof containers might be given the same treatment (washing) to remove external dust. Food which had been irradiated would not itself be radioactive and would be safe to eat so long as the fallout were washed off. Even unwrapped vegetables might be safe to eat if a supply of clean water were available for washing them. And the longer you waited after an attack, the less you would have to fear from fallout because the radioactivity diminishes quite rapidly as time goes by. Nevertheless you would have to be careful, because nobody could be sure whether some areas might not be more highly contaminated than others. A sudden down-pour of rain, for example, could bring large quantities of fallout down in one place and make the surroundings dangerously radioactive for several months, not just two weeks.

Surviving a limited attack

It should be mentioned, however, that a very limited attack would give different survival possibilities from a large one. Shelter living would not be any easier for people surviving in the fewer 'fringe areas' but more people would find themselves in places unaffected by the attack. Unfortunately there might be great uncertainty about whether the limited attack would be followed by a large one. People living in the path of a fallout plume would be able to escape the radiation risk by evacuating, but *only* if they knew that no further warheads were expected. Limited attacks could either end a war or simply set the scene for escalation into massive attack and counter attack. Government reports and broadcasts could draw the wrong conclusions about whether the bombardment was at an end, so many people in fallout areas would still not know what was the best thing to do

The uncertainties about the effects and the likely outcome of nuclear war are no less great for sheltering than for anything else. Conditions might be favourable: a fresh, strong wind from over the ocean, for example, might remove fallout from the air above centres of population. Those sheltering might survive in their millions. On the other hand it is equally possible that most attempts at self protection would prove futile. Whatever happened, however, most of the factors deciding your fate would be beyond your control: it is indeed unreasonable to expect that delicate human bodies could easily be protected against the brutish violence of nuclear weapons.

7 The moment of crisis

It might not be easy to recognise when the world is about to be plunged into a nuclear holocaust. For one thing there must always be a very remote possibility that a surprise attack could be mounted. It is also possible, but again highly unlikely, that nuclear war might begin by accident: a large variety of safeguards against this have been devised, including the 'hot line' from Washington to Moscow, but under exceptional circumstances something could go wrong: accidental nuclear war cannot be totally discounted. It still seems likely in the 1980s that any nuclear war would either involve the superpowers directly, or be orchestrated by them, despite the proliferation of countries building nuclear weapons. So developments in the Soviet Union and the United States are more likely to influence the decision of whether to 'cross the nuclear threshold' than events elsewhere. Political problems in trouble spots around the world might certainly lead to conventional war, but it seems likely that these could only escalate to nuclear conflicts if to do so served the interests of the superpowers.

The most likely way in which nuclear war might start would be if one superpower became convinced that the other was about to use nuclear weapons. This could only be at a time of extreme international tension, and with accurate news coverage many individuals would be able to spot the danger signs. The Government might wish to persuade the media to tone-down the reporting of and commentary on the approaching crisis, and with good reason: they would not wish to provoke the potential enemy into making a first strike by advising everybody to prepare some form of protection. If America evacuated, for example, the Soviet Union could become convinced that the President was about to order an attack, and might strike first to achieve the advantage. This political brinkmanship does not help individuals to decide whether war is imminent: they would have to 'read between the lines' of current affairs news reporting and make up their own minds about the magnitude of the threat.

Although there are now several candidate 'theatres' of nuclear war, only one has a sophisticated pattern of deterrence, a wide variety of nuclear arms and what amount to agreed 'ground rules' between the superpowers for the conduct of nuclear warfighting. This of course is Europe. Because strategic war between the superpowers is still seen as the 'top rung' of the escalation ladder, politicians prefer to talk in terms of more limited nuclear confrontations, at least for the initial stages of any war. This is because these are far more credible than suggesting that either side would readily begin a full-scale, or even limited, strategic war. The hope is that a limited war, confined to a single theatre, might be all that would be needed to settle matters between the superpowers should they find negotiations fruitless. In the game of deterrence it is of the utmost importance that threats be believed. The Soviet Union can believe that NATO would use limited numbers of tactical nuclear weapons in Europe, and the United States can believe that the Soviet Union might also do so. And this plan of action also brings us back to Europe as a potential trigger point of a nuclear war between the superpowers.

The superpowers have the greatest respect for each other's threats. If NATO threatened to use tactical nuclear weapons to repulse a Warsaw Pact invasion of West Europe the Soviet leaders would take them at their word, and with justification: as things stand at present NATO, who have less conventional strength, might be compelled to do this if the Warsaw Pact decided to advance with conventional forces. Equally, although the Soviet leaders would not want to start a nuclear war it is understood that they would certainly do so if they felt circumstances demanded it.

To make this mutual respect possible, to make the threats believable and thus to make nuclear deterrence work, a wide range of war-fighting strategies has been evolved for Europe. One of the latest is the NATO plan to base ground-launched cruise missiles (GLCMs) in Europe from about 1983. This illustrates that NATO means business: cruise missiles and the improved Pershing ballistic missiles, soon to be based in West Germany, can reach Moscow from their European launch locations. (The Stockholm International Peace Research Institute (SIPRI) calls them 'Eurostrategic' weapons because they could act as an extension to the United States' strategic triad.) As such they represent a 'middle rung' on the escalation ladder and an important part of the NATO flexible response strategy which, as Britain's Ministry of Defence states, 'maintains enough forces at each level to convince the Russians that they could not hope to gain an easy victory'.[1] This makes it quite clear that nuclear weapons are for war fighting and that this is the most effective means of war deterring. Tactical nuclear weapons such as short-range ballistic missiles and heavy artillery could be used as the most limited initial form of nuclear attack. If these failed to repulse the Russians NATO plans to use the 'smaller medium range weapons' (ie GLCMs and Pershings) to 'bring home to the Russians the appalling risks they would run if they pressed us further. The aim of using them

would be to persuade the Russian leadership – even at the eleventh hour – to draw back.'[2]

The 'eleventh hour' would presumably be at a higher stage of escalation, *after* the use of short-range tactical weapons had failed to repulse a Warsaw Pact advance over West Europe. Clearly the use of strategic weapons such as cruise missiles and the new Pershings would be against the Soviet Union directly, and not confined to the European theatre. Soviet leaders would have expected NATO to use the 'Eurostrategic' weapons. If they had intended to retreat or surrender at this stage it seems doubtful that they would have begun a campaign in the first place, so it is very difficult to believe that war would halt without further escalation. At any stage (and all stages might happen swiftly – within minutes) there might be a counterforce strike by one superpower aimed at (largely) disarming the other. It is truly difficult to imagine how either superpower would be able to retire gracefully to lick its wounds at *any* stage of escalation short of at least such a 'limited' counterforce attack.

Crucial to the whole matter, of course, is whether this avalanche of plausible events would be started off by military aggression (conventional or nuclear). From time to time the United States and the Soviet Union issue 'warnings' to each other. In response to the Afghanistan crisis of 1979 the United States made only token gestures to the Soviets: including an Olympic Games boycott and a grain embargo. But when internal disturbances in Poland began about a year later American threats, warning Russia not to intervene militarily in Poland, sounded distinctly more warlike. Most people must fear the moment when a threat, from either superpower, cannot be withdrawn: when a military confrontation becomes inevitable. Only then will it be proven whether NATO's flexible response policy is a recipe for swiftly ending a war without escalation, or might inevitably lead to global war.

Dr Edward Teller, the scientist usually known as 'the father of the H-bomb' writes that 'the destruction of human life has

Thousands of ICBMs, such as this Soviet missile, are maintained in readiness by the superpowers.

always been limited by the willingness of people to stop killing, rather than by physical inability to slaughter'.[3] If nuclear war began, therefore, we would have to hope that the adversaries would call a halt to the slaughter. We would also have to hope that the decision to do so was made within seconds of the 'nuclear threshold' first being crossed, because from that moment on deterrence would have failed: 'victory' would probably go to the side able to assess the situation soonest and react the quickest.

What sort of events might overtake an average person or group if deterrence in Europe broke down and nuclear war escalated?

The Jackson family living in Chaddesden, a suburb of Derby in the English Midlands, would possibly have become aware of a growing political confrontation between East and West in Europe, perhaps taking place along with a deteriorating world econ-omic recession. They might have heard reports of warlike threats, but these could have been displaced from 'front page' coverage by pressing domestic issues. The West, and presumably the East, would be anxious to play down the crisis in the hope that this might lead to a better climate for negotiations. The issue might drop from public awareness altogether for a few days or weeks, but meanwhile both sides might be preparing for war. At any stage negotiations might prove successful, and if so the Jacksons might hear no more about the crisis. (Neither NATO nor the Warsaw Pact would be anxious to publicise a stalemate for fear of disturbing the uneasy peace which might follow.) If, however, the nuclear threshold were crossed, and if all 'levels' of deterrence failed, the family might find that with only hours or minutes of warning a full scale war had begun.

If this happened and a 150-kt device were detonated above Rolls Royce Aero Engines workshop on the southern edge of Derby, the citizens could rapidly be divided into three categories: those killed by immediate bomb effects, which might include parts of the predominantly industrial southern flank of the city; those who by accident survive unscathed, such as commuters whose homes are in the Peak District hills 10 to 20 miles to the north (they might survive if the attack took place at night time, but some people could be killed by a daytime attack during the working week), and thirdly there would be those, perhaps including the Jacksons, who might be on the fringes of areas of devastation who had been able to take some protective measures which could save their lives.

Most people in Chaddesden might have made no preparations at all to defend themselves against nuclear attack. On receiving the attack warning the Jacksons might fill all available containers with water, hurriedly whitewash windows and (if time permitted) cover them with adhesive tape. Next they might barricade windows and doors of at least one inner room with furniture, drawing the curtains and sealing the window area as much as possible to protect against flying glass.

When the bomb exploded the family living 4 miles north of the Rolls Royce factory (the city centre lies between 'ground zero' and Chaddesden) would see a brilliant flash of light and feel the pulse of heat. It would seem as if the sun had suddenly been placed only a few miles away from them.

There would be hardly any abnormal sounds for a pregnant twenty seconds – the blast wave taking this length of time to reach Chaddesden – but before the blast wave arrived anybody out of doors might have clothes ignited by the heat flash and could suffer second degree burns on exposed skin. South-facing parts of the house with windows not white-washed or otherwise covered might be set ablaze.

With a roar like a combination of an earthquake and a hurricane the blast wave would arrive. At more than 2 psi 'over-pressure' it could shatter every window in the house. The roof could be demolished and doors blown in, but brick walls might remain standing. A few houses in the Jackson's street might nevertheless be flattened altogether by the blast, with neighbours dead or trapped in the ruins.

There would be a rush of wind: at 70 miles an hour stronger than ever before experienced in Chaddesden. Television aerials would be blown down, shattered glass from the ubiquitous broken windows would fly in all directions for half a minute or more, together with roof tiles, leaves and branches from trees, loose wood, garden tools and a multitude of other objects and debris. Anybody outside and many people indoors could receive multiple lacerations from flying glass or life-threatening injuries from heavier fragments and falling masonry.

Many houses in the area might be set ablaze, and some would be completely gutted. If the Jacksons climbed upstairs and looked south through one of the holes where a window had been blasted out they would see a picture of desolation. A mushroom cloud several miles high and wide would be forming over the former Rolls Royce works minutes after the blast. Fires in Derby's Eagle shopping centre, started by the heat impulse, might be extinguished, especially on the side facing the blast, by 200 mph winds. Fires to the north of the Eagle Centre, in the demolished Council House, Cathedral and Police Station, could remain alight, despite 130 mph winds, and a massive 'conflagration' might spread towards the Technical College and then on to Duffield to the north.

In Chaddesden the Jacksons could only guess whether the fires would eventually span the Water Meadows or the Race Course to reach them. The wind direction and weather could critically affect this. Derby's surviving population would hope for a rainstorm to put out the fires which if unchecked could cause more widespread devastation than the blast.

There would be no crater from such an 'air-burst', neither would the fireball touch the ground. Fallout would consist of a very fine dust formed from fission products and bomb materials intimately mixed together. This would be so light that it would rise high into the atmosphere and would not fall on Derby. But survivors in Derby and nearby places could not be sure that there would be no fallout hazard if they were not told. So they might spend the next hours and days in dread of radiation, and indeed might be exposed to fallout resulting from ground-burst explosions elsewhere in the country which had been blown in Derby's direction by the wind.

Everybody would want information about what had happened and how to keep themselves alive, but the television stations would almost certainly not be broadcasting and mains electricity would be off so TV sets would not work. Radio Derby's studios near the city centre would be flattened, and despite thorough government plans for a network of wartime radio transmissions the Jacksons might not be able to find any BBC station (whether or not it was under the control of WTBS, the Wartime Broadcasting Service) functioning. The full horror of what had happened might first be revealed by a short-wave broadcast from All India Radio's external service, followed (perhaps after a few days) by medium wave domestic broadcasts. Only then might the Jacksons be able to guess what the future might hold in store for them.

8 The aftermath

The outcome of a nuclear war would be totally remote from anything experienced in the past. Americans have never endured the levels of civilian casualties that are possible with even the most limited form of nuclear attack. During the Second World War, the Soviet Union, Japan and Poland suffered levels of devastation and loss of life which it is often said are comparable with those possible today from limited nuclear attacks. The fact that such countries have been rebuilt despite massive losses is sometimes cited as grounds for optimism about the possible outcome of nuclear war. But no such optimism is justified. At the end of the Second World War the United States was completely unscathed, world trade hardly faltered and the planet was unpolluted, rich in resources and able to support the restructuring of individual countries decimated by the war. A country might hope to recover from almost any level of destruction with the support of trading partners and allies. After a major nuclear war any countries unscathed and relatively uncontaminated would be hard put to survive, let alone lend aid across the world.

It is also questionable whether the destruction suffered in the Second World War was truly comparable with what might result from a limited nuclear attack. Nuclear weapons produce large amounts of collateral damage: a bomb destroying a munitions factory might also raze a city and spread hazardous fallout hundreds of miles across the country. Nuclear attack might begin and end within a few hours: the devastation in the Second World War took place over several years. The fear and panic induced by such an attack would be incomparable with the emotional response to conventional, more familiar weapons.

It might prove possible to rebuild society after nuclear attack; it might prove possible to limit such attacks and prevent escalation, but nobody can know.

A typical family, the Smiths of Palo Alto in the San Francisco area, live their lives dependent on others. Factories and businesses function efficiently because many people cooperate with others. Supplies of electricity, gas, oil and coal for domestic and industrial consumption are available because other people make sure the supply is maintained. Hospitals, the police force, the fire service and schools supply other basic services which depend on the cooperation of many different people. The Smiths hire a plumber to repair the central heating, take the car to a mechanic to get it serviced and depend on the work of countless other professionals for most daily needs. The high standard of living they and other Americans enjoy is only made possible because specialists do jobs they are trained for, instead of individuals trying to provide all their needs from their own skills and resources. Palo Alto is a typical example of an academic, business and industrial centre in a developed country maintained by cooperation between fellow citizens. This could be destroyed after most types of nuclear attack.

Interdependency goes further than the boundaries of a country, however. America imports many manufactured goods and raw materials while relying on exports to

Tactical nuclear bombs are intended for 'battlefield' fighting. United States marines were able to practise charging an 'objective' during a weapon test at Yucca Flat, Nevada, in the 1950s.

finance these imports. If international trade came to a halt after a nuclear war Americans might suffer even more than other countries, being the world's leading trading nation.

The destruction of the principal industrialized countries could send the world's economy into a downward spiral from which it might not be able to recover soon enough to avoid mass starvation and hardship on a scale unimaginable. The world as a whole has developed to the extent that humans can only continue to survive by trade and cooperation, but there are also limits to the extent to which global resources can be exploited. The delicate ecosystem of our planet which is today only just capable of supporting the human race might be so damaged by nuclear war that our viability could be lost, and we might follow the dinosaurs down the road to extinction.

Different levels of attack would have different effects upon the target and upon the societies which surround and support them. As final illustrations of the longer-term effects of nuclear weapons, we return to the four case studies introduced in Chapter 4 and imagine what subsequent events the Smith family of Palo Alto, California, might experience.

1. Aftermath of the San Francisco attack

If the attack on San Francisco took place in the evening, before the Smiths had gone to bed, their first idea that something was about to happen might be the sudden interruption of television programmes broadcast from the San Francisco area. There might be no time for the television studios to transmit the message that a four-minute warning of missile attack had been received. Air-raid sirens could sound in Palo Alto, radio stations might begin to broadcast a warning that attack was imminent. At this stage it might not be clear that San Francisco was the intended target, and the Smiths would have no idea whether more bombs might follow.

Suddenly night would be turned into day for several seconds with a blinding white light (created by the fireball) shining from the direction of San Francisco, which lies 25 miles to the north-west of Palo Alto. Two minutes later the Smiths would hear the tremendous roar of the blast wave produced by the nuclear explosion which might shatter many of the windows in their area. If the wind were blowing at a typical 10 mph from the direction of San Francisco the Palo Alto area would start receiving radioactive fallout within two hours.

The first stunning, numbing shock would be terrifying. After believing for decades that nuclear weapons exist to deter war, not for making real explosions and killing millions of people, they would be emotionally shattered by the psychological hammer blow of the destruction of their belief. Panic could prevent them from acting logically, and yet rational and speedy actions would be essential for self protection: the stark message from radio news broadcasts would be a warning that within two hours they must protect themselves against fallout.

Today's nuclear arsenal could leave thousands of 'Hiroshimas' throughout the civilised world. Towns and cities could be destroyed by vengeful acts in a war which could never be won.

Mr and Mrs Smith might themselves be trembling with fear, yet to keep the family alive they would have to make quick decisions and actions, at the same time perhaps soothing fearful children and a crying baby.

They would want to know whether to leave home and get out of the path of the deadly fallout blowing towards them from the San Francisco direction (their house could be dangerously radioactive for months afterwards) or to stay at home and try and build a protective shelter in the basement or a downstairs room. Many television stations would be unable to continue transmissions and the telephone lines would be jammed with millions of people all over the country trying to find out what was happening. There would be power cuts, perhaps temporary, possibly permanent, and the family might have to continue preparations in semi-darkness by candle or torch light.

Provided the Smiths' transistor radio was working, however, radio broadcasts (perhaps under government supervision) would instruct them to stay at home, warning that roads in the Bay Area were needed for the emergency services (and the army) and perhaps saying that numerous bottleneck traffic jams had already built up around Palo Alto, threatening to leave desperate car occupants stranded in the open, completely exposed to the radiation and unable to escape from the area of severe contamination.

Mr and Mrs Smith might therefore decide that the best course of action would be to follow government instructions (relayed from the surviving local radio stations) and select the most protected room in their house as a fallout room, within which they could construct a refuge, as described in *Protection in the Nuclear Age*.

To their horror they might discover that no room in the house had all the window panes intact. At 25 miles from a ground-burst explosion of 1-Mt, the blast over-pressure is sufficient to destroy most window panes. The main problem would thus be one of keeping fallout dust from entering the uncovered window-space. Referring to instructions in official literature and listening also to the radio broadcasts, the family might shift tall wardrobes and other furniture over the window space in a downstairs room. They would look for wood, plastic, cardboard: anything to block up the gaping holes which very shortly would allow the deadly dust to enter their room. They might break down with nervous exhaustion, almost giving up the seemingly impossible task of keeping the fallout as far away from them as possible.

If they managed to retain their composure, they might succeed in blocking up the broken windows of one room completely, pushing furniture in front of them, bringing sturdy tables in and piling heavy materials on top of them to form a protective shield. If Mrs Smith's mother lived with the family, she might be recruited to fill buckets and saucepans with water and bring these, together with other essential supplies, into the fallout room as fast as her ageing, rheumatic joints could carry her.

Amid the sheer terror of knowing that they would have to stay in this make-shift shelter, using a bucket for a toilet and eating whatever foods they had managed to stock which do not perish quickly or require much cooking, they would be even more apprehensive about the future. Would the next bomb fall on Palo Alto? They would have no way of knowing, and the confusion about whether the San Francisco bomb was an isolated act of war or whether it was soon to be followed by many more explosions would not abate for hours, days, or perhaps weeks.

Outside the Smith's house in the streets and avenues of Palo Alto there would be a cacophony of familiar yet strangely different sounds: neighbours' voices, calling, screaming, shouting; distant police and ambulance sirens; dogs barking, cats howling and babies crying pitifully. If Mr Smith went to talk with neighbours he might receive conflicting reports about what had happened and about what would be the best thing to do. Some would be loading up cars, despite the government warnings. The fear and panic might turn neighbour against neighbour and fights could break out. Many would be courageous and react stoically. Whatever their attitude, the overall outcome would be the same: just two hours after the explosion, anybody remaining out of doors would risk becoming lethally contaminated with fallout. He or she would probably not be welcomed into any shelter because people would not want to add to their own risk. So two hours after the explosion there would be a mad final rush for shelter, then a deathly hush would overtake Palo Alto and the whole of the downwind Bay Area. If the Smiths heard their doorbell ring they would agonise about whether to reply and admit a contaminated stranger into their fallout room who might bring death to all.

There would be little hope of sleep under the fearful, cramped shelter conditions of the first night. Following more detailed instructions from the radio 'Grandma' and the parents would probably agree to stay on the side of the inner refuge nearest to the window and hence with the least protection from radiation. The children, being more susceptible to radiation injury, would stay furthest from the window. Knowing that the hazard was greatest during the first two days the parents might forbid anybody to leave the room for at least 48 hours. They would all have to use the improvised toilet, placed near the door, though one of the adults would regularly remove the plastic 'liner' bag and take it out of the room, risking exposure to a higher level of radiation for a few seconds for the sake of removing the awful stench.

By morning the children might be enjoying the novelty of the situation a little, but this would not last long because they would soon become frustrated by being restricted to living in a part of just one room. Outside there would be silence, except perhaps for the wind rattling the garage door and some finches unknowingly greeting the morn with joy, already condemned to a protracted death from radiation sickness. Cats and dogs left outside might be whimpering and howling with pain, vomiting and passing diarrhoea mixed with blood, fatally ill.

Examining the food and water stocks, the Smiths would perhaps find that they did not have enough to last two weeks. The radio broadcasts might suggest that after 48 hours under shelter they could consider leaving the fallout room for a few minutes at a time to perform tasks which at the expense of some risk from radiation, could save their lives. One of the adults could go to the bathroom to cover the bath which had been hastily filled with water before the fallout arrived. If there seemed to be sufficient quantities of drinking water in the hot water tank and the central heating system, it might be decided to try using the lavatory, flushing the previous two days' waste down it. Finding the mains water still working the Smiths might decide to use the toilet and risk brief exposure to radiation rather than tolerate the dreadful bucket latrine. A news item could perhaps inform them that mains water in the Palo Alto area was almost completely free from fallout. Although stored water would still be preferred for drinking, the risk of exposure to fallout from mains water used for other purposes would be small. This would make a great difference to shelter life as the Smiths could wash down areas thought to be contaminated with fallout dust. They could even point a hose-pipe out of a window and begin to hose down the paths and walls of the house in an attempt to decontaminate these, but any such activities would of course also bring the hazard of exposure to radiation.

After a few days, however, despite the greater level of comfort and hygiene made possible if mains water were safe to use, Mr Smith might be suffering from early symptoms of radiation sickness: vomiting and tiredness. They would not know whether this was the beginning of a fatal illness or perhaps simply a response to the mental exhaustion and physical shock. Trying the telephone the Smiths could perhaps by this time be able to talk with friends and relatives. This would boost morale to some extent, but on the other hand it could also bring a sense of hopelessness as they discovered how enormous the impact of a single nuclear explosion had been psychologically and physically on California and the rest of America. Many friends in the area might be suffering from radiation sickness, and if Grandma Smith fell ill, developing a fever, there would be genuine fear for her life.

The days would drag on. Nothing would improve quickly because all available emergency personnel would be needed to help in the San Francisco area where people would have multiple injuries, burns and bereavement together with the destruction of homes and buildings to cope with as well as the fallout problems.

The air in the shelter room would become fetid through lack of ventilation. Family members might begin to lose hope and remain in a listless stupor much of the time. If Grandma Smith died from old age made worse by exposure to radiation, the family might not react with normal grief at their bereavement, their emotions sapped by the recent experience. They might not know what to do with the body. Day by day the impact of the death might prey on them and they would perhaps feel extreme sadness and guilt.

Use of the radio might have to be rationed to save the batteries, but the eventual restoration of mains electricity would be a mixed blessing: the house would begin to function as normal, but television programmes might reinforce the sense of profound shock as the Smiths learned more about the explosion. They would yet again be instructed to stay at home and not to go out of doors perhaps for two weeks or even more after the attack.

If rain storms began they would be pleased to know that a great deal of fallout dust would be washed away into the gutters and conduits where it could do little harm. But they would perhaps find that rain water was coming into the house through broken windows and holes in the roof bringing radiation inside along with the damp.

When life in the San Francisco peninsula slowly began to return to normal (or as normal as possible) the Smiths would probably feel a continued sense of deep shock. The attack might have been very limited (possibly for the purpose of demonstrating determination, to make a 'deterrent' posture credible) but life would be permanently changed. People would know for the first time that the policy of nuclear deterrence, on which they had based their hopes for continued peace had failed. They would realise that another nuclear attack might happen at any time and would know from television and radio broadcasts as well as from their own experience (if they chose to visit the devastated San Francisco city much later) that a single warhead can cause a truly immense amount of damage. They would know that thousands of warheads could be launched against the United States and whereas previously this knowledge had almost no meaning (especially as it was considered to be a very remote possibility), it might be a constant source of fear. It could become obvious to the Smiths, their friends, colleagues and neighbours that if a warhead were to explode on Palo Alto almost no practical level of protection might help to save lives. They would learn that buried blast-resistant shelters could protect people for several weeks, but these might never be provided out of public funds because of the expense. Apart from the cost, the local authorities would want to concur with national policy and refrain from building blast-resistant shelters because, they could argue, to do so might provoke an attack. The Smiths might decide that blast shelters are not the answer, and that they, like most people in the area, would not in fact feel they would give enough protection.

Realising that protection was impossible they might take a far greater interest in political decisions concerning nuclear weapons. Whether or not the attack was the fault of the Government, Americans would probably lay some of the blame at the feet of the incumbent President, removing him or her from office at the next election.

If the Smiths had previously been in the habit of driving to Sausalito, their journey could take nearly twice as long after the attack, with parts of the Bayshore freeway and most of San Francisco's roads impassable and the entire approach to Golden Gate bridge perhaps razed to the ground. Parts of the centre of San Francisco would remain dangerously radioactive for several years. Roads and buildings might not be reconstructed in the original locations, indeed town planning all over the country could favour designs for new housing developments scattered over as wide an area as possible. Property values in central city areas might plummet, but rural locations would probably enjoy an unprecedented boom.

If the attack proved to be an isolated one with no further explosions elsewhere in the world it might conceivably do some good in the long term, acting as a spur to the United Nations and other international agencies to press for more agreements on disarmament as a matter of urgency. It might initially bring about the signing of a 'total test ban treaty'. Although this would not stop countries from manufacturing weapons along well proven existing designs it would at least be a step in the direction of world disarmament, though far more progress than this would be needed to substantially lessen the risk.

Unfortunately, however, it is not easy to see how an isolated attack against a single city might prove sufficient to end a war. It is far more likely that such an attack would be part of a more comprehensive military strategy. So fear of further attack among the Smiths, other Californians and fellow Americans, would be well justified.

2. An attack against oil refineries

The Smiths would soon learn from radio broadcasts of the horrific levels of destruction and slaughter at and around oil refineries across the United States, which in California are almost all close to residential or industrial urban areas. A huge segment of Los Angeles inland from the harbour would be set ablaze by the attack against the cluster of oil refineries situated there. The inferno could easily spread and consume the entire Los Angeles conurbation if

Fierce, uncontrollable fires could break out after an attack against an oil refinery.

weather conditions permitted. In Palo Alto the Smiths would count themselves lucky to be separated from the worse blazes (near Richmond and Martinez over 30 miles to the north) by the San Francisco Bay, but the plight of their friends in Berkeley, Oakland and other eastern Bay locations would be desperate with perhaps a wall of flames advancing from the blazing refineries further north which might raze the whole area. Even in Palo Alto windows would be shattered, and as the full complement of eight warheads carried by the SS-18 ICBM would not be needed to guarantee destruction of refineries, several warheads might be detonated in the San Francisco peninsula to increase the impact of the attack.

The Smiths would not be able to find out whether friends and relations living in some of these areas were dead or alive for several days or perhaps even weeks after the attack. Phones probably would not work and radio broadcasts could only give more general information. Although Palo Alto would not have been directly hit the Smiths might fear fallout initially, staying at home, keeping children indoors and wondering what to do. Should they shelter or not? Local officials might not have enough information at first to give advice, and everybody would be afraid of further attack.

As soon as people began to realise that fallout radiation would not affect Palo Alto there would almost certainly be a frenzy of activity with everybody stocking up with food and supplies. But there would be a constant fear of renewed attack, nobody would know what the future held in store, nor would they know precisely what preparations might help keep themselves alive. There would be confusion and panic.

If the Smiths dared to venture out to stores they might find long queues or just empty shelves, and despite government reassurance that there would be no fallout hazard and that further attack was unlikely everybody would be anxious and emotionally stunned. All dust would be suspect even though everyone knew there was no fallout danger. Many stores would be closed, others might bravely introduce rationing systems and prices would certainly rocket, indeed nobody would know whether currency held any value: most would adapt to trading by means of barter to obtain essential goods.

A week after the attack they could learn, for example, that the fire at Los Angeles harbour had spread eastwards, fanned by strong westerlies, razing much of Long Beach, Santa Ana, Anaheim (obliterating Disneyland) and neighbouring areas, but perhaps sparing Los Angeles' International Airport and much of the northern areas of the city.

The psychological impact of the knowledge that millions of people had died in the explosions and flames, with perhaps millions more seriously injured, burned, or dying, might never be forgotten and would make everybody fearful for the future, especially of the prospect of a further attack.

Like many other Americans the Smiths would want to help victims in the disaster zones. But they would fear to leave home and there would be no gasoline or diesel fuel. Overnight road and air transport might be brought to a halt. Unlike the national response to an attack against a single city in which maximum resources (however inadequate) might be mobilised to help the survivors, it would not prove possible to mount significant rescue operations for the much greater disaster of an attack against oil refineries. Fires would rage unchecked: fire-fighting facilities would be hopelessly over-stretched. Survivors could be left entirely without help especially if it were not known that the explosions were air burst.

As the days went by Palo Alto citizens would hear broadcasts describing horrific scenes of corpses being buried by the hundreds in mass graves, and huge numbers of burns victims slowly dying without medical care or even pain killing drugs.

After a few days Palo Alto might see a trickle, then a flood of refugees from the stricken areas, many of them wounded or burnt, others with severe psychological disturbances, children without parents, parents who have lost children: virtually nobody without bereavement. There might be no facilities for these newcomers.

Some would have to be billeted in various public buildings appropriated at short notice, others might be taken in by families. An atmosphere of post-attack comradeship might help a great deal at first, with Palo Alto families only too willing to help the miserable refugees. It would only be a matter of time, however, before the welcome wore thin and resentment, jealousy and sheer overcrowding brought intolerable social problems: husbands and wives might fight or separate, frightened men, women and orphans would perhaps form gangs to scavenge and steal. If looting and theft escalated the police would have to use the emergency powers given them by the State Government for suppressing criminal activities and Federal troops could be called in: they would certainly be prepared to use their weapons.

Mr Smith's place of work, which might be a 'fast food' restaurant along El Camino Real, would close down through lack of fuel, food supplies and customers (who would no longer be able to drive there through lack of gasoline). Joining thousands of others in Palo Alto now unemployed, Mr Smith might receive ration books and food stamps rather than dollars for social security payment, as the value of currency would be in doubt. Mrs Smith would no longer be able to reach her lecturing job 20 miles away at the University of San Francisco.

Electricity would have to be cut altogether for weeks or months after a successful attack against oil refineries because coal and other energy sources could not meet the demand. Exceptions might be made for a few hours at a time to make vital pieces of industrial equipment work, but domestic electricity supplies would probably be switched off.

Even though the attack had produced no fallout, the Smiths would either think about evacuating from the Bay Area or would start to protect their house against further attack, hoping that no bomb would land close enough to cause serious damage. Any escalation of the war, however, might happen before they had time to complete such preparations. And even if they blocked up windows and strengthened the house as much as possible, a full-scale attack would probably kill them by blast or fire.

It would take several weeks or months free from explosions, together with confirmation from the Government (or from an invasion force) that hostilities were at an end, before the Smiths would stop preparing for war and begin to plan for a peaceful if doubtful future.

There would be a shortage of energy for transportation, industry, electricity generation, home-heating and aviation, and there might be little prospect of supplies being resumed. People with the expertise needed to rebuild refineries might have died because they were close to the explosions. Farmers could be denied their usual supplies of pesticides and fertilisers. Without these agricultural inputs, and with no fuel for tractors, machinery or trucks, the capac-

ity for feeding the nation after this attack would be much reduced. Neither might America be able to buy food from overseas: countries normally exporting food to the United States might also be attacked and there could be an economic problem caused by rocketing inflation, and the collapse of the dollar as an international currency. It might be a long time before adequate trading arrangements could be set up with other countries still in a position to conduct trade, and by that time Americans might begin to starve.

Although there would be plenty of food after the attack most of this would quickly have disappeared from the stores because of panic buying. Stocks of food in warehouses could not be shifted because of a shortage of gasoline and diesel fuel. Mass starvation might be averted by swift government action, but food stores would be protected by armed guards. Anybody who had not followed government instructions might be denied ration books, social security benefits and medical facilities and be given no help in finding accommodation.

The Smith family might have to resign themselves to a diet of cereal and dried legume-based foods, with hardly any meat or fresh vegetables because of the transport problems. Even if scarce fuel reserves could be allocated for food distribution, the truck drivers and store keepers bringing the food to the public would have to be paid in some form other than cash. This would bring many problems and would certainly slow down the process of food distribution.

Cars would become useless, and would have no prospect of having their tanks filled perhaps for several years after the attack. Bicycles would be highly prized, but could not even partially restore the levels of personal mobility enjoyed up to the time of the attack.

3. A limited counterforce strike

A limited counterforce strike against America would affect the Smiths very differently from an attack purely against oil refineries. Although cities would not be targeted, almost every house in the Bay Area would have windows shattered and perhaps millions living close to military targets would die as buildings collapsed and fires raged out of control.

The attack could begin without any warning: ballistic missiles would be chosen for attacking the military targets because these could not be shot down. Aircraft and cruise missiles could be used for other attack strategies after air defence systems had been eliminated. But in the limited counterforce attack considered in Chapter 4 only actual nuclear weapons based on American soil are attacked, which indicates the probability that only intercontinental ballistic missiles would be used. Sirens might not sound, nor broadcast warnings be given: just one flash after another, many in quick succession, lighting the sky brighter than the mid-day sun and filling the air with blast waves ranging from distant rumbles to ear-splitting crashes.

The counterforce strike might take no more that a few minutes to complete. An extended attack would give the American forces time to retaliate, defeating the object of the attack. If the Smiths dared to look out from their partially shattered house they would see a red glow lighting the sky to the north: the awesome result of thousands of square miles enveloped in flames. A huge part of California, especially the San Francisco area, might be razed by the incendiary effect of several air-burst weapons targeted on air bases or detonated in time to bring down airborne bombers and strike aircraft scrambled by the Air Force seconds before the first warheads arrived.

The main worry in California from a counterforce attack would be fallout. If westerly winds prevailed throughout the attack and for several days afterwards, the massive cloud of radioactivity from surface-burst weapons on the ICBM fields (east of California) would be blown away from the state, although onto Americans on the East Coast. But the Smiths and other residents of Palo Alto would worry about fallout from *all* explosions, not just from those at the missile fields. Everybody would be confused, not knowing whether San Francisco was at risk of fallout contamination or not, and people would live in terror of the next wave of

Victims of the Hiroshima bomb. Despite severe injuries and radiation sickness, few survivors would in reality get any help from medical or emergency services.

bombing. If the United States retaliated there would almost certainly be worse to come: people would be panic-stricken and terrified, and with just cause. Nobody would be able to give reassurance that an end to the horror was in sight.

In fact the Smith family would have good reason to fear fallout. They would feel anxious in case the fallout plumes from the Montana missile field (more than 700 miles north-east) or from the Arizona field (a similar distance south-east) might be blown in their direction. Experts might assure them that most of the dust would fall to earth before it could travel so great a distance, but knowing that about 2,000 ground-burst bombs might be detonated in middle America they would fear that some of the colossal amounts of radioactivity might, perhaps because of freak winds, travel to California. But quite apart from fallout from the missile fields, however, the Smiths would be only too well aware of the military presence in the Bay Area and the likelihood that bases would be targeted. Although it is not necessary in *theory* to detonate weapons on the ground to destroy targets other than missile silos, there are good reasons for fearing that surface bursts might be used: underground headquarters and arms dumps might be attacked with surface detonations, many warheads might accidentally explode at the wrong altitude, and some warheads might be deliberately intended to produce fallout as a means of disrupting the American war effort to the maximum. So what would Palo Alto residents do?

If the Smiths were alive after the attack and if they could overcome their instinctive feelings of panic, they could at least begin preparations for fallout protection. The first problem, however, would be the broken windows. The official calculations about shielding from gamma rays and the protective factor of different buildings and improvised shelters makes the assumption that no fallout is swallowed or inhaled. In fact with many windows shattered by the large counterforce attack most survivors would run a severe risk of touching fallout dust, getting it on their clothes or hair, swallowing or inhaling it. The broken windows would make it extremely difficult to keep the dust out of partially destroyed or even otherwise intact homes. Fallout rooms and inner refuges might be constructed which were no more than a pitiful parody of the idealised designs appearing in *Protection in the Nuclear Age* and other official information. Many people would not realise the extreme danger from ingested fallout which was threatening them. In parts of the country unaffected by fallout people would survive. In less favoured regions, many would die from hopelessly inadequate fallout protection. Deaths would be protracted. Apart from the fatigue, sickness, vomiting, diarrhoea, fever and haemorrhage produced by the generalised effects of radiation sickness, victims would have horrible sores and burns from contact with beta-emitting fall-

out dust, and might develop open festering wounds infected by bacteria which could not be checked by the body's weakened defences against disease.

Undoubtedly mortality rates would be high in any area downwind of the prime military targets. If the weather were kind, blowing the fallout away from most populated areas and preferably washing it away by a goodly sprinkling of rain, the fallout effects might be far less severe than otherwise. But few people would be able to protect themselves adequately. In *practice* the panic and hysteria could frustrate all efforts during the few hours before the lethal cloud of fallout began to reach downwind areas.

If we presume that the Smiths had the strength of will and self-composure necessary to act rationally amid the crisis we could envisage that they would manage to build some sort of fallout protection. But most of America might also be affected by fallout, and the radio stations might have ceased broadcasting, as well as the television network, so there would be few government instructions, perhaps none at all, and possibly no information about what had happened. The Smith family would face the horrors and discomfort of sordid, filthy shelter living for an unpredictable period of time. If they did not possess radiation measuring equipment they would just have to wait two weeks (if they survived that long) and then consider emerging to try to live on in the wrecked country around them.

They would almost certainly not have the benefit of uncontaminated mains water; there would perhaps be no mains water at all. They could expect no help from the Government for many weeks, and perhaps none for months or years. Any medical problems would have to be dealt with in the shelter room themselves, however severe these might be, and when the food and water ran out whatever the radiation risk they would have to try to find supplies.

It might not be safe to emerge from the shelter after two weeks, however, and the family, in common with many other Palo Alto residents, might run into many of the problems mentioned in Chapter 6. Everybody would be frightened. Fallout protection for most people would probably not be good enough in the areas of heaviest contamination. If the Smith family had inferred beforehand that an attack was possible they might have succeeded in making more fallout preparations than most other local people. When it became safe for them to emerge, however, they might find that the state's traditionally stable, friendly, predictable social climate had been transformed into desperate chaos.

Working life could have become almost completely disrupted, with businesses, universities and offices all closed down, and because of this friends and colleagues would lose contact with each other. Regular meetings of the district officials, voluntary bodies, social services, church congregations and charitable societies might all be abandoned. Lack of communications would hinder progress towards restoring the social cohesion which would be necessary for any kind of recovery to begin. People might feel alienated from each other, especially as many would be starving.

As conditions became more desperate serious crimes might follow, and there might be little prospect of government control to restore law and order. Police officers, for example, would fear for the well-being of their own families and would be reluctant to patrol the streets protecting other people's property and lives when the Government might no longer be able to pay them in meaningful terms (currency being of doubtful value) and might not even retain real control over the nation. Only individual courage and community spirit might save the day on a few occasions, though it is too much to expect that most ordinary human beings would be capable of the superhuman acts of self-denial and altruism necessary in many instances to avoid extreme social disruption.

The Smiths might be among the thousands forming long queues at Stanford University Medical Center and other local hospitals. Most of those waiting could be suffering from radiation sickness, and if they were lucky a medical auxiliary or volunteer would walk down the line advising such people to go home and not waste their time in the queue. The hospitals would be unable to offer them any treatment. Only a token medical gesture at helping the plight of some victims could be made. Apart from the local victims mostly suffering from untreatable radiation sickness, there could be a growing tide of refugees from other parts of San Francisco and elsewhere in California: bomb victims arriving in the hope of getting medical treatment for severe burns and multiple fractures. Some might be lucky, but most would be turned away.

The medical services might have to organise 'triage' – the system whereby cases have to be divided into three categories: those who will die whether or not they receive treatment, those who will recover without treatment (including perhaps people with quite serious injuries such as fractured limbs), and those who with treatment might be kept alive. Only the last category might receive any medical attention at all: even then it would probably be from a volunteer auxiliary. Doctors and nurses would be performing drastic surgical and medical procedures as fast as possible to try to save some lives. But the task could be beyond the limited facilities and medical personnel available.

Farming in the area could be severely hit by fallout. Very few farm animals could be given sufficient indoor protection to prevent radiation sickness. Those left to graze outside might eat huge amounts of fallout and die within days or weeks from radiation sickness. It might take several months before most of America's farm animals had died or were slaughtered because of radiation sickness, so the Smiths could be surprised a month or so after the attack to find plentiful supplies of fresh meat in the shops: the farmers might have been able to take quick action to limit the suffering of their animals, while at the same time carrying on a little trade by selling the meat. Provided the offal and skins contaminated with fallout were discarded the meat would be safe to eat. This temporary glut, however, would foreshadow the forthcoming absence of meat from the national diet as land would mostly be used for producing crops for direct

The initial effects of blast, fire and terrific winds would sear and batter everything in their path: a scene from *The War Game,* a BBC television documentary widely regarded as an accurate portrayal of the grim reality of nuclear exchange.

human consumption after the attack. Lost herds would in any case be difficult to replace quickly even if the land or animal feeds could be obtained.

Milk would be shunned for months or years even if cows survived, because of the possibility of contamination with radioactive iodine and strontium-90 (an isotope which gets trapped in bones and can form a life-long hazard of cancer for growing children).

If the attack took place in the springtime, shortly after planting, crops could be almost totally destroyed, their development being halted by radiation. An attack causing heavy fallout just before the harvest would also result in heavy crop losses because of the radiation dangers to farm workers. At other times of the year crop losses from fallout exposure would not be so great, since the radiation hazard falls quite rapidly week by week, and although by peacetime standards the fields might be considered dangerously radioactive, risks would have to be taken after a nuclear attack.

If both crops and animals suffered from the counterforce strike, the Smith family would view the future anxiously even if Palo Alto were not damaged. They would fear food shortages, particularly in the uncertain economic aftermath of the attack.

If the war ended, the older members of the family might be recruited into local 'decontamination brigades'. These would be volunteers who would put themselves at some risk of radiation exposure to decontaminate countless public buildings. They would have to sweep and hose schools, churches and offices and demolish buildings where effective decontamination could not be done. The aim would be to make Palo Alto citizens safe from the risks of developing diseases such as cancer, leukaemia and genetic illnesses from long-term exposure to radiation. Needless to say some members of the decontamination brigade would become victims of such radiation effects themselves.

4. A large attack

A large attack would produce levels of death and destruction which are so overwhelming that they defy adequate description. The Hiroshima and Nagasaki explosions gave a foretaste of the consequences of using nuclear weapons for warfare. Today it is clear that only a minority would survive a large attack. The 12.5-kt Hiroshima bomb would be classed as a small weapon today, equivalent in yield to many of the thousands of tactical weapons currently deployed in Europe. The hypothetical attack on America considered in Chapter 4 consists of 4,000 warheads: many of them of 1-Mt yield, *80 times* as powerful as the 1945 Hiroshima bomb, others could be several megatons, each one capable of destroying a city the size of Washington DC or Detroit, in just a few seconds.

The Smith family would almost certainly be within range of immediate bomb effects from such an attack, which might include targets such as the NASA Ames Research Center nearby at Moffet Field, or the Stanford Research Institute in Menlo Park. One very likely possibility is that they would die, crushed flat by a pile of bricks while filling the bath with water and trying to improvise some fallout protection. Alternatively, one or more members of the family might live for days, trapped beneath falling masonry, dying without any hope of rescue from the multiple effects of burns, injuries and radiation exposure.

Many other Bay Area citizens might be trapped by fire, and would either be burnt to death or die from suffocation. Some who had invested in costly nuclear shelters before the attack might be suffocated in their shelters or roasted by the intense heat of a fire-storm or conflagration. Some might survive, only to find later that the entire area had been reduced to a radioactive ashpit.

Estimates of precisely how many Americans could survive such an attack vary widely. If populations were neither warned nor prepared, the deaths within 30 days could approach 90 per cent throughout the country. Casualties could be much lower, and in theory it is true that quick reactions, evacuation and good improvised fallout protection could reduce casualties significantly, so that more than half of the American population would survive at least one month after the attack. But what would be the effects of an attack on an America almost completely unprepared? Inevitably most citizens would die. Neither could civil defence promise any big improvement in long-term survival. Nuclear weapons are highly destructive; 4,000 or more could detonate in a first salvo against the United States, and the resulting destruction could not fail to be immense.

If one or more of the Smiths happened, largely by chance, to be among the few survivors they would be lucky to remain sane as they learned the extent of the devastation. The attack on America would almost certainly not be isolated. It would probably be just part of the complete destruction of, at the very least, Europe, the whole of North America and the Soviet Union. Surviving Smiths might have to revert almost to the stone age in their living habits, although it might be possible that they could use some stores of goods manufactured before the holocaust.

Any survivor might reflect on the fact that the war-fighting policies of the 1980s were developed because it was recognised that the large attacks implicit in the mutual assured destruction relationship were unacceptable, making nuclear war unthinkable. The more limited war-fighting strategies, however, might have proved merely to be the starting point from which each higher rung on the escalation ladder became thinkable and indeed inevitable. The end result might be the same holocaust, the same unimaginable waste of life, simply arrived at by a different route.

Afterword

Nuclear weapons are one of the great paradoxes of our times. On one hand, they have not been used in anger in more than three and a half decades. While millions of people have died during that period in wars around the world, none has been killed by a nuclear weapon. The central concept of deterrence is awful – that neither side will use nuclear weapons because both know that the other could wreak damage without precedent in retaliation. Yet nuclear deterrence has been stable. And it is likely to remain so. The reason is simple: nuclear weapons will continue to be different from any weapons the world has ever known, and they will be so regarded by political leaders. While military planners may construct, and eager strategists may believe in, plans for 'limited nuclear war' or 'limited counterforce strikes', none of that will be persuasive to heads of state contemplating a step into the nuclear abyss. What will be uppermost in their minds is the possibility that *any* use of nuclear weapons will run beyond control, unleashing Armageddon.

On the other hand, nuclear arsenals continue to grow. In 1977 the United States and the Soviet Union had some 14,750 nuclear warheads between them; two years later that figure was 17,750. Nuclear weapons the size of those that devastated Hiroshima and Nagasaki are now regarded as relatively small. And so the paradox of nuclear weapons produces an alternation in the public mind: much of the time, the nuclear situation seems relatively stable, and is, moreover, too awful to contemplate, and is thus dismissed; at other times, however, it seems more and more likely that some time, somehow, a nuclear weapon will be used, and the fear grows.

The fear is growing now, for reasons that are not hard to find: Western concern over the Soviet nuclear build-up, reflected in decisions to increase Western nuclear arsenals, including the deployment of cruise missiles in Europe; changing nuclear strategies that appear to contemplate 'limited' nuclear wars; the evident failure of arms control efforts, especially between the superpowers, by comparison to the hopes of a decade ago; and the equally clear increase in tension and uncertainty in international politics. Nuclear issues serve, almost by their nature, as a kind of barometer of confidence, not just among nations but within them.

In these circumstances, Peter Goodwin's analysis is timely. It is thoughtful and careful in an area where scaremongering is all too easy and all too frequent. The probability of a nuclear weapon being used, or even of a nuclear war, is not zero, but neither is it very great. Increasing tension and nuclear arsenals suggest that the chance may be greater now than in the past, but other developments go in the opposite direction – for instance, more sophisticated command arrangements probably have diminished the risk of a nuclear war by accident.

He also provides perspective for the critical issues of public policy that confront all of us. He outlines a number of simple steps individuals can take to give themselves a small margin of protection. That most of us do not take those steps reflects implicit judgements – correct in my view – both that nuclear war is not very likely and that the margin of safety would be very small.

More important is the issue of government policy toward civil defence. That civil defence now commands support all across the political spectrum is a sure indication that concern over nuclear weapons has increased. That makes it all the more important to be clear about what civil defence can – and cannot – do. As Peter Goodwin points out, large-scale government programmes to build shelters probably are not sensible public policy for Britain and most other countries, given cost and given the destructiveness of existing nuclear weapons. Planning sensibly for evacuation is a more promising ap-proach. Yet even there the limitations are severe. Much of Britain, like most of the American East Coast, simply is too densely populated to make widespread evacuation feasible within likely warning times. Nor is the situation in the Soviet Union a much happier one, since its population and industry are slightly more concentrated than those of the United States.

The most important task of public policy will remain the same in the future as it has been throughout the nuclear age: not preparing to survive nuclear war but preventing it. Even if the awful logic of nuclear deterrence still seems relatively stable, that can hardly be taken for granted as security concerns change, nuclear technology moves on, and nuclear arsenals spread. The focus of public attention should be on what it will require to sustain de-terrence. There, too, the debate too often is full of easy simplicities. For example, we all want nuclear arsenals reduced, but a focus on numbers does not always make sense as an arms control priority: when nuclear weapons number in the thousands, small reductions matter little, and other measures may do more to add stability to deter-rence; and even large reductions could produce more uncertainty than any clear benefit.

Gregory Treverton

Glossary

ABM See Anti ballistic missile.

Air burst If the fireball produced by a nuclear explosion does not touch the ground (detonation having taken place in the atmosphere) the explosion is described as an air burst.

Anti ballistic missiles (ABM) For attacking approaching missiles in order to destroy them before reaching the target.

Alpha particles The nuclei of helium atoms (stripped bare of electrons). They carry an electric charge and can penetrate less than one millimetre through body tissue.

Atom A unit of matter consisting of a single nucleus carrying a positive electric charge surrounded by negatively-charged electrons equal to the number of protons in the nucleus. Everything is made from atoms.

Atom bomb See Fission bomb.

Ballistic missile A rocket with one or more warheads mounted on it, which is shot out of the earth's atmosphere. It can accelerate to about 15,000 miles per hour (24,000 km/h) and can thus fly between continents in about 20 minutes.

Beta particles Electrons which have been freed from atoms or created by a nuclear reaction.

Blast wave The enormous pressure which builds up within a fraction of a second at the point of a nuclear explosion is the source of a high-pressure blast wave which pushes air outwards causing tremendously strong winds.

Chain reaction When a fissionable nucleus captures a neutron and fission occurs, several fresh neutrons are formed and these in turn can cause fission in other nuclei nearby. A chain of fission reactions can then take place.

Circular error probable The estimate of the accuracy of a weapon system: the radius of a circle (the centre of which is the target) within which 50 per cent of the missiles targeted are likely to fall.

Civil defence Measures designed to protect the civilian population in any emergency, be it natural disasters or war.

Counterforce Strikes or strategies against nuclear weapons and the systems they rely on to work efficiently, such as command and communication stations.

Critical mass The minimum amount of fissionable material needed to sustain a chain reaction.

Cruise missiles Unmanned miniature aircraft designed to carry warheads – either nuclear or conventional – and fly at very low altitudes and subsonic speeds.

Delivery system The means by which weapons are delivered to their targets. They include shells, bombs and missiles and can be fired from silos, aircraft, submarines and guns.

Deterrence theory The theory that war is deterred because each side knows that the other possesses huge numbers of nuclear weapons and thus understands the dire consequences of initiating a nuclear exchange. See Mutual assured destruction, Overkill.

Deuterium Often called hydrogen 2, deuterium is an isotope of hydrogen. It is used in nuclear bombs when it reacts with tritium to produce a fusion reaction.

DNA (Deoxyribonucleic acid) The large organic molecule that carries genetic information. It can make exact copies of itself.

Electromagnetic waves High-energy waves associated with electric and magnetic fields which travel through space at 186,282 miles per hour (299,731 km/h).

Electron A constituent of the atom, it carries a negative charge, has a very small mass (about 1/2000 that of the proton) and moves around the nucleus of the atom.

Element The simplest forms of matter that can be identified by chemical means. All atoms of the same element have the same number of protons in the nucleus, the same number of electrons moving around the nucleus and hence the same chemical properties.

Fallout See Radiation, delayed.

Fireball Almost immediately a nuclear bomb is exploded in the atmosphere a spherical fireball is formed which rapidly expands and cools to form a mushroom-shaped cloud.

Fission When atoms are split apart fission occurs. The atom's nucleus breaks up into two smaller pieces and several neutrons and releases energy. Fission may occur spontaneously or be induced by bombarding neutrons.

Fission bomb A nuclear bomb which explodes when atoms are split apart.

Fission products The 300 or more different isotopes which can be formed when fission takes place.

Fusion When two nuclei of a light element, such as the hydrogen isotope deuterium, fuse together to form a nucleus of a heavier atom fission occurs.

Fusion bomb A nuclear bomb which explodes when atomic nuclei are fused together.

Gamma rays Waves similar to x-rays but shorter, more energetic and capable of causing more damage to the material which they penetrate. It needs several feet of lead to stop them.

Genes The hereditary factors present in cells, which consist of sections of DNA.

Ground burst See Surface burst.

Ground zero The point on the ground or, in the case of an air burst, directly beneath it, which is the centre of a nuclear explosion.

Half-life The length of time any particular radioisotope takes for half of its atomic nuclei to transform themselves into the nuclei of other atoms by emitting radiation.

Half-value thickness The thickness of material needed to reduce the intensity of a beam of gamma radiation to one half of its strength.

Hardened Weapons and installations particularly vulnerable to nuclear attack are protected by hardened structures (eg made of thicknesses of reinforced concrete) which are often underground and can only be destroyed by direct hits or very close strikes.

Heavy water Water in which the hydrogen is replaced with deuterium. The early hydrogen bombs used heavy water, as do some nuclear power reactors.

Helium One of the lightest elements, helium is formed when nuclei of hydrogen are fused together, releasing a great deal of energy. This what happens in a hydrogen bomb.

Hydrogen When the nuclei of the lightest element – hydrogen – are fused together a great deal of energy is released. This is what happens in a fusion or hydrogen bomb. The isotopes of hydrogen, deuterium and tritium, can also be used to create nuclear bombs.

Hydrogen bomb See Fusion bomb.

ICBM See Intercontinental ballistic missile.

Inertial navigation A computerised navigational system which establishes whether the missile is on course and makes any adjustments necessary to improve the accuracy of its flight path.

Intercontinental ballistic missile (ICBM) Missiles which can be delivered to a very distant target (eg one in another continent).

Ionization Static electricity among the atoms of any material radiation passes through.

Isotopes Each atom of an element has the same number of protons in its nucleus, and therefore similar chemical properties, but the number of neutrons can vary. These variants are called isotopes of an element.

Kiloton (kt) Explosive energy equivalent to 1,000 tons of TNT.

Kt See Kiloton.

LD 50 The dose of any particular substance which would be lethal for approximately one half of the group exposed. The LD 50 of radiation is about 450 r.

MAD See Mutual assured destruction.

Megaton (Mt) Explosive energy equivalent to one million tons of TNT.

MIRV See Multiple independently targetable re-entry vehicle.

Molecules Collections of atoms.

Mt See Megaton.

Mutual assured destruction (MAD) Nuclear deterrence between the USA and USSR based on the theory that if one side strikes the other can cause reciprocal retaliatory damage on a large scale.

Multiple independently targetable re-entry vehicle (MIRV) Missile carrying more than one warhead, each of which can be independently targeted.

NATO See North Atlantic Treaty Organization.

Neutron One of the basic particles out of which the atom's nucleus is made. It carries no electricity and can penetrate body tissue deeply.

Neutron bomb A very small fission bomb which is triggered by compression. Most of its energy is delivered in the form of high-speed neutrons which are lethal to people, but do little blast and heat damage, leaving property relatively unharmed.

North Atlantic Treaty Organization (NATO) One of the two major nuclear military alliances, comprising Western European and North American countries. Belgium, Britain, Canada, Denmark, France, Greece, Iceland, Italy, Luxembourg, the Netherlands, Norway, Portugal. Turkey, the United States and West Germany are NATO members.

Nucleus Every atom contains a nucleus consisting of positively charged protons and uncharged neutrons. (Ordinary hydrogen is an exception and carries no neutron.) The nucleus is nearly 2,000 times heavier than the accompanying electrons.

Overkill The ability of the two superpowers (USA and USSR) to destroy each other many times over. See also Deterrence theory, Mutual assured destruction.

Overpressure Pressure over normal atmospheric which is 14.7 pounds per square inch.

Partial Test Ban Treaty A treaty banning nuclear weapon tests in the atmosphere, in outer space and underwater signed in 1963 by the British, American and Soviet governments, and since by 109 other countries.

Plutonium A by-product of nuclear power processes, plutonium is formed artificially, being the residual material after uranium 238 is converted to uranium 239. It is fissionable and can be used in fission bombs.

Proton A constituent of all nuclei, carrying a positive charge of electricity, equal and opposite to the negative charge carried by each electron.

R See Roentgen.

Rad The unit used to describe how much energy is absorbed in a material when a particular amount of radiation passes through it.

Radiation Electromagnetic waves (gamma rays and x-rays) and particles (alpha particles, beta particles, neutrons) produced by the explosive energy of nuclear fission and nuclear fusion processes.

Radiation, delayed The fission products present in the weapon debris which emit radiation (mainly gamma rays and beta particles (electrons) over a long period.

Radiation, initial The flash of radiation produced at the time of a nuclear explosion consisting of highly-penetrating and invisible gamma and x-rays. It can be very intense but its range is limited.

Radiation sickness Usually the first sign of radiation exposure, it is caused by damage to the gastro-intestinal tract, and will, on average, result from accumulated doses exceeding 150 roentgens.

Radioactivity The property possessed by the nuclei of some atoms of disintegrating or decaying spontaneously.

Radioisotopes Unstable isotopes produced when nuclear fission takes place.

Rem The unit used to describe the amount of radiation required to cause a particular amount of biological damage in a human.

Roentgen (r) The unit used to describe the amount of ionization produced when radiation is absorbed in air.

SALT See Strategic Arms Limitation Talks.

Seven-tenths rule Many radioisotopes have very short lives and it is estimated that seven hours after a nuclear explosion the amount of radiation is only one-tenth as much as one hour after the detonation.

Strategic Arms Limitation Talks (SALT) Agreements between the USSR and USA limiting strategic weapons.

Strategic weapons Those weapons which can be delivered to a very distant target, one in another continent for example.

Sonar detection Sensors laid on the sea bottom which scan the oceans for submarine noises and vibrations and thereby pin-point their locations.

Tactical weapons Intermediate-range (but not necessarily intermediate in yield) weapons intended for use in a particular theatre or region.

Terminal guidance A system (for example a laser or radar) to guide the warhead fired from a ballistic missile onto its target, after re-entry into the earth's atmosphere.

Theatre weapons Weapons with a short range, down to a few miles, intended for battlefield use. They have low yields.

Tritium Often called hydrogen 3, tritium is an isotope of hydrogen. It is used in nuclear bombs where it reacts with deuterium to produce a fusion reaction.

Uranium The heaviest naturally occurring element uranium has an unstable isotope – uranium 235 – which can disintegrate causing nuclei to split, releasing neutrons, which in turn can trigger off a chain reaction. This is what happens in a fission or atom bomb.

VLF Radio system using very low frequency waves for communicating with missile-carrying submarines.

Warsaw Pact One of the two major nuclear military alliances, comprising the Eastern Bloc countries (USSR, Bulgaria, Czechoslovakia, East Germany, Hungary, Poland and Romania).

X-rays Short, energetic electromagnetic waves capable of penetrating materials.

Notes and references

Chapter 1

1. Office of Technology Assessment, *The Effects of Nuclear War*, Allanheld, Osmun & Co, Montclair, NJ 1980, pp. 144–5.
2. This contains assumptions about the unknown numbers of tactical warheads and stored warheads.
3. *The Effects of Nuclear War*, p. 3.
4. In practice, of course, it has never been tried. Such factors as high winds or rain in the target area or unsuspected 'bumps' in the earth's gravity field could push even today's accurate missiles off course.
5. Stockholm International Peace Research Institute (SIPRI), *World Armaments and Disarmament: SIPRI Yearbook 1979*, Taylor and Francis, London, 1979, p. 427.
6. Eyewitness report quoted by Earl Mountbatten of Burma in an address to the Stockholm International Peace Research Institute in Strasburg, 11 May 1979.

Chapter 2

1. The USSR exploded a device with a yield of approximately 57 Mt on 30 October 1961 on the island of Novaya Zemlya, in the Barents Sea.
2. The second SALT agreement was signed by the USSR and USA in June 1979, but has not yet been ratified by either side. The treaty will establish equal limits on the total number and kinds of strategic nuclear delivery systems, restrictions on certain new strategic weapons and provision to improve verification of the treaty.
3. *SIPRI Yearbook 1979*, p. 399.
4. Inertial navigation itself is liable to be inaccurate because it relies on the gravity of the earth which can vary from place to place in a manner not anticipated.
5. One of the smallest known CEPs is that of the US Minuteman II missile which, when the current upgrading is completed, will be about 600 feet.
6. The source of this and the following calculations in this chapter of physical weapon effects is Glasstone, Samuel and Dolan, Philip J. (eds), *The Effects of Nuclear Weapons*, 3rd ed., US Government, Washington DC, 1977.

Chapter 3

1. Medical Research Council, *The Hazards to Man of Nuclear and Allied Radiations*, Her Majesty's Stationery Office, London, 1956, p. 12.
2. Ibid, p. 85.
3. Ibid, p. 53.
4. Ibid, p. 18.
5. Ibid, p. 19.
6. Ibid, see for example pp. 15, 19, 20, 21, 22.
7. Ibid, p. 20.
8. Ibid, p. 23.

Chapter 4

1. This is in fact a generous estimate. *SIPRI Yearbook 1979*, p. 394, gives a figure of 15 per cent.
2. *The Effects of Nuclear War*, p. 144.
3. *Cruise Missiles*, a pamphlet published by the Ministry of Defence, London, 1980.
4. *SIPRI Yearbook 1979*, p. 449.
5. Ibid, p. 427.
6. Private source.
7. *The Effects of Nuclear War*, p. 144.
8. The first weapon would use a low airburst explosion so that the second warhead could reach the target without being destroyed by ground debris drawn into the fireball. The second detonation would then be a ground burst for maximum overpressure effect.
9. *The Effects of Nuclear War*.
10. *The Military Balance 1980–1981*, International Institute for Strategic Studies, London, 1980.
11. Published in *The Effects of Nuclear War*.
12. Ibid, p. 65.
13. Ibid, p. 141.
14. Ibid, p. 8.

Chapter 5

1. Integrating the area under the dose rate curve gives approximately three times the unit time dose rate.

Chapter 6

1. *The Effects of Nuclear War*, p. 142.

Chapter 7

1. *Cruise Missiles.*
2. Ibid.
3. Edward Teller, *The Pursuit of Simplicity*, Pepperdine University Press, Stanford, 1980.

Bibliography

Selected bibliography

Cristy, G. A. and Kearny, C. H., *Expedient Shelter Handbook*, Oak Ridge National Laboratory, Oak Ridge, 1974.

Defense Civil Preparedness Agency, *Protection in the Nuclear Age*, Department of Defense, Washington DC, 1977.

Glasstone, Samuel and Dolan, Philip J., *The Effects of Nuclear Weapons*, 3rd ed., US Government, Washington DC, 1977.

Home Office, Central Office of Information, *Protect and Survive*, Her Majesty's Stationery Office, London, 1980.

Home Office, Scottish Home and Health Department, *Nuclear Weapons*, 3rd ed., Her Majesty's Stationery Office, London, 1974.

Katz, A., *Economic and Social Consequences of Nuclear Attacks on the United States*, US Senate, Committee on Banking, Housing and Urban Affairs, 96th Cong., 1st Session, March 1979.

Medical Research Council, *The Hazards to Man of Nuclear and Allied Radiations*, Her Majesty's Stationery Office, London, 1956.

The Military Balance 1980–1981, International Institute for Strategic Studies, London, 1980.

National Academy of Sciences, *Effects of Multiple Nuclear Explosions Worldwide*, Washington DC, 1975.

Office of Technology Assessment, *The Effects of Nuclear War*, Allanheld, Osmun & Co, Montclair, NJ, 1980.

Stockholm International Peace Research Institute (SIPRI), *World Armaments and Disarment: SIPRI Yearbook 1979*, Taylor and Francis, London, 1979.

Sullivan, Roger J., et al, *Civil-Defense Needs of High-Risk Areas of the United States*, Final Report Revision A, System Planning Corporation for Defense Civil Preparedness Agency, Washington DC, 1979.

Further reading

Alexander, Peter, *Atomic Radiation and Life*, 2nd ed., Penguin, Harmondsworth, 1965.

Akimov, N. I. (ed.), *Civil Defense*, Oak Ridge National Laboratory, Oak Ridge. This was originally published in Moscow in 1969 and was analysed by Professor Leon Gouré in the Canadian *Emergency Planning Digest*, Jan/Feb 1978.

Ayers, R.U., *Environmental Effects of Nuclear Weapons* (3 vols), Hudson Institute, New York, 1965.

Bidwell, S., *World War III: a Military Projection*, Hamlyn, London, 1978.

Bulletin of the Atomic Scientists is published monthly. Their address is 1020–1024 East 58th Street, Chicago, Illinois 60637.

Calder, Nigel, *Nuclear Nightmares*, BBC, London, 1979.

Chinnock, Frank W., *Nagasaki: The Forgotten Bomb*, George Allen and Unwin, London, 1970.

Cox, J., *Overkill*, Penguin, Harmondsworth, 1977.

Gouré, Leon, *Soviet Civil Defense in the Seventies*, Advanced International Institute, Washington DC, 1975.

Gouré, Leon, Kohler, Foy D. and Harvey, Mose L., *The Role of Nuclear Forces in Current Soviet Strategy*, Center for Advanced International Studies, Miami, 1974.

Griffiths, Franklyn and Powani, J. C., *Dangers of Nuclear War*, University of Toronto Press, Toronto, 1980.

Hersey, John, *Hiroshima*, Penguin, Harmondsworth, 1966.

Iklé, F. C., *Every War Must End*, Columbia University Press, New York, 1971.

Iklé, F. C., *The Social Impact of Bomb Destruction*, University of Oklahoma, Norman, Okla., 1958.

The International Institute for Strategic Studies, London, publishes *The Military Balance* and *Strategic Survey* annually, *Survival* six times a year and the *Adelphi Papers* series.

Jane's Weapon Systems are published annually by Macdonald and Jane's Ltd, London.

Japan Broadcasting Corporation (eds), *Unforgettable Fire*, Wildwood House, London, 1981.

Jungk, Robert, *Brighter Than a Thousand Suns*, Penguin, Harmondsworth, 1964.

Laurie, Peter, *Beneath the City Streets*, Panther, London, 1979.

Organski, A. F. K. and Kugler, Jack, *The War Ledger*, University of Chicago Press, Chicago, 1980.

Robinson, Julian Perry, *The Effects of Weapons on Ecosystems*, Pergamon Press, Oxford, 1979.

Smith, D., *The Defence of the Realm in the 1980s*, Croom Helm, London, 1980.

Thompson, E. P. and Smith, Dan (eds), *Protest and Survive*, Penguin, Harmondsworth, 1980.

Report to the United Nations, *Effects of the Possible Use of Nuclear Weapons and the Security and Economic Implications for States of the Acquisition and Further Development of these Weapons*, United Nations, New York, 1967.

Acknowledgements

An intense team effort was mounted by the staff of Ash and Grant to distil and concentrate the range of information for this book. Ian Grant, Mary Trewby, Nick Maddren and Valerie Richards all worked with an exceptional dedication and enthusiasm, without which the quality of content, style and format could not have been achieved. Many original ideas came from joint discussions with the team; so did the emphasis of the book and decisions about which facts (out of many) are of the greatest importance to individuals living under the threat of nuclear war.

The team shared a feeling of responsibility that accurate facts be made available in a style which can be understood by the non-specialist. This was also the attitude of Peter Sharfman of the US Office of Technology Assessment who took the trouble to read an entire draft of the book and to level detailed, valuable criticism in the light of his own research. Candid 'off the record' consultations with the British Home Office and Ministry of Defence were a great help, as were similar discussions with officials in the United States. Talks with Roger Sullivan of the System Planning Corporation in Arlington, Virginia, contributed an immense imput of knowledge about civil defence and evacuation.

Arthur Katz generously discussed the findings of his US Senate report on 'Economic and Social Consequences of Nuclear Attacks in the United States'. The Astronomer Royal, Professor Sir Martin Ryle, also read and criticised the book. His comments from an objective scientific view point were refreshing and illuminating. Discussions with Gregory Treverton of the International Institute for Strategic Studies in London and Jonathan Medalia of the Congressional Research Service in Washington, DC, both of whom also checked an early draft, have enriched the book.

However, the final responsibility for the opinions expressed and the accuracy of the information printed in this book rests, of course, with me and no factual error or emphasis of interpretation can be attributed to any of the invaluable assistance rendered by the people mentioned above.

Peter Goodwin, London, April 1981

Picture credits

Peter Addis/New Scientist: 81 top left and right

BBC Copyright Photographs/National Film Archive: 113

Boeing Aerospace Company/MARS: 10; 12; 21 bottom; 22 bottom

Crown Copyright (MOD – RAF)/MARS: 22 centre

E.C.P.–Armées/MARS: 20 top right

FMS/MARS: 19 bottom

Facs Ltd: 78 top

Eugene Fleury: 23 (reference: Stockholm International Peace Research Institute, *SIPRI Yearbook 1979*); 50–1; 54–5; 57 (reference: *Times Atlas of World History* published by Times Books, London, 1978); 58; 67; 69; 70

Jackson Day Designs: 78 bottom (reference: Gouré, *Shelters in Soviet War Survival Strategy*, Advanced International Studies Institute, Washington DC); 79; 80 top; 81 bottom; 82; 83; 84; 85; 86–7 (reference: Cristy and Kearny, *Expedient Shelter Handbook*, Oak Ridge National Laboratory, Oak Ridge); 90

Keystone Press Agency: 13; 21 top; 24 top; 24 bottom right; 30; 37; 99; 102; 103; 107

Richard Lewis: 15; 16; 17 (reference: Berzins, *Nuclear Weapons*, Pan, London, 1966); 25; 26 (reference: Berzins, *Nuclear Weapons*); 33; 34; 35 (reference: Kevin N. Lewis, 'The Prompt and Delayed Effects of Nuclear War', *Scientific American* July 1979, New York); 38 (reference: Berzins, *Nuclear Weapons*); 41 top (reference: Peter Alexander, *Atomic Radiation and Life*, Penguin, Harmondsworth, 1965); 41 bottom

Luwa Ltd: 80 bottom

Kevin Maddison: 39; 77 (reference: Berzins, *Nuclear Weapons*); 91; 93

Martin Marietta Aerospace/MARS: 19 top

Paul Popper Ltd: 23 top right; 24 bottom left; 110

Rand McNally: 65

Science Photo Library: 11

US Air Force/MARS: 9; 11

US Army/MARS: 20 bottom

US Department of Environment/Science Photo Library: 64

US Navy/MARS: 22 top; 23 top left; 53

Warsaw Photographic Agency/MARS: 20 top left

The publishers would like to thank Wildwood House for permission to use the quotations from *Unforgettable Fire*, and Taylor and Francis for permission to use quotations from *SIPRI Yearbook 1979*.

Index